D1060539

Persistent Persecutory States of the Elderly

Persistent Persecutory States of the Elderly

FELIX POST, MD, FRCP, DPM
*Physician, The Bethlem Royal Hospital
and the Maudsley Hospital, London*

PERGAMON PRESS
OXFORD · LONDON · EDINBURGH
NEW YORK · TORONTO · SYDNEY
PARIS · BRAUNSCHWEIG

Pergamon Press Ltd., Headington Hill Hall, Oxford
4 & 5 Fitzroy Square, London W.1

Pergamon Press (Scotland) Ltd., 2 & 3 Teviot Place, Edinburgh 1

Pergamon Press Inc., 44–01 21st Street, Long Island City,
New York 11101

Pergamon of Canada, Ltd., 6 Adelaide Street East, Toronto, Ontario

Pergamon Press (Aust.) Pty. Ltd., 20–22 Margaret Street, Sydney,
New South Wales

Pergamon Press S.A.R.L., 24 rue des Écoles, Paris 5e

Vieweg & Sohn GmbH, Burgplatz 1, Braunschweig

First edition 1966

Library of Congress Catalog Card No. 66-25608

PRINTED IN GREAT BRITAIN BY A. WHEATON & CO. LTD., EXETER

2961/66

Contents

Introduction

The background and results of the investigation reported in this monograph may be stated briefly for the reader's general orientation.

During "crabbed old age", many people are said to become unduly sensitive, bitter and suspicious. Surveys have suggested that a small proportion of old persons (perhaps 4 per cent) could be classified as "eccentric", but that the occurrence of frank paranoid psychoses was rare. While acute persecutory states associated with delirious reactions are not uncommon at all ages, persistent paranoid illnesses not related to an affective psychosis or to a chronic brain syndrome are responsible for only a small proportion of psychiatric admissions after the age of 60: estimates vary between 8 and 16 per cent. However, in the past, few of these patients were ever discharged, and because they were usually in much better physical health than dements or depressives, elderly paranoid psychotics tended to survive in mental hospitals for long periods. Also, speaking to community workers concerned with the welfare of old people, one gains the impression that paranoid conditions are a good deal more common and troublesome than has been suggested by medical and psychiatric surveys.

The introduction of the phenothiazine and other "psychotropic" drugs has for the first time held out some hopes of a curative treatment in late schizophrenia or paraphrenia. Basing himself on clinical work with over 100 patients, the writer has tried to discover to what extent and under what conditions the course of these illnesses can be influenced therapeutically. Furthermore, investigations of the paranoid syndromes of old age were in the past largely descriptive and taxonomically orientated, but drug therapy has introduced an experimental dimension to the present study.

Its two main results may be anticipated here. Provided phenothiazine therapy can be carried out and maintained effectively, few elderly patients exhibiting schizophrenic symptoms fail to remit completely, or to be relieved of their most troublesome disturbances. Of wider implication is the suggestion arising from this study that the persecutory syndromes of late life present a continuum of related conditions, many of which can also occur much earlier. They may best be regarded as results of the same pathological developments which under certain, more unfortunate conditions, produce the schizophrenias of young persons.

Acknowledgements

I have drawn heavily on the help of numerous people who cannot all be named—first and foremost junior colleagues, nurses, and social workers. I am particularly indebted to Dr. A. E. Maxwell for statistical advice, to Miss Nona Hemsley for carrying out the computations, to my wife for stylistic criticisms, and to Mrs. D. Wingent for preparing the final typescript.

CHAPTER 1

Background of the Study

Persecutory beliefs and experiences arise in many human situations, and with the exception of extreme youth, at all ages. Paranoid ways of perceiving and thinking are encountered only where there exists awareness of the subject's own personality in relation to others, as well as a modicum of introspection. There is general agreement that paranoid personality traits and paranoid symptoms in psychological disturbances increase in frequency after the middle of life, and by the time old age is reached, people tend to suffer more and more often from disabilities and circumstances which are known to be conducive to the development of sensitive suspiciousness at all ages: e.g. belonging to an underprivileged group, loneliness, and deafness. In addition, elderly persons are particularly prone to develop states of diminished awareness leading to faulty perceptions and misinterpretations, which are so frequently paranoid in character. Patients with subacute, rather than acute and severe confusional states (or brain syndromes) usually function well enough intellectually to construct under certain circumstances elaborate systems of false beliefs. These paranoid states will vary in degree of logic and tenacity with the level of cognitive impairment. Like the underlying cerebral disturbances (due to toxins, deficiencies, oedema, etc., see Post, 1965) they will be transitory. Progressive and unremitting cerebral deterioration sooner or later leads to a degree of mental impairment which precludes the creation and maintenance of a system of elaborate false beliefs. However, a proportion of patients hover for many months near the ill-defined borders between subacute and chronic confusion, when their cognitive dysfunctions are still variable and their defects somewhat patchy. Very much like younger persons with alcoholic Korsakoff psychoses or incompletely cured GPI, these patients with incipient pre-senile, senile or arteriosclerotic dementias sometimes exhibit more persistent paranoid symptoms.

The present study is not concerned with transitory persecutory states, but solely with elderly persons who suffered from persistent paranoid disorders. In a few, there were proved and significant anatomical brain changes; in some, the presence of pathological processes could not be definitely excluded; but in most, the paranoid disorder was not associated with any demonstrable cerebral disease or deterioration. We attempted to exclude all patients whose persecutory symptoms appeared to have been associated with melancholic or manic disorders, as these features vanished following recovery from what was considered to have been the basic affective illness. At the time, we were not fully aware of the intricate way in which the affective and the schizophrenic reaction types can mingle, especially in the elderly—a matter which will arise again later.

Reviewing previous work on paranoid disorders in late life, their association with organic psychoses has been frequently described and discussed in the past, and, like others, the present author has attempted to link previous personality structure to paranoid symptomatology in dementia (Post, 1944, 1965). There has almost certainly been in the past a tendency to regard all non-affective paranoid illnesses in old age as early dementias, largely on account of an axiomatic belief that schizophrenic illnesses (dementia praecox!) could not possibly occur for the first time in life during the involutional or senile periods. Bleuler (1943) reviewed the literature on the late schizophrenias, by which he meant illnesses differing little from those seen earlier in life, but starting after the age of 40. Many of the publications summarised by Bleuler are rather inaccessible now, but to judge from the frequent use of the term "praesenilis" (which in those days referred to the age range 40–50!) hardly any of the patients described would have been over the age of 60. Kleist's (1913) 10 cases of involutionsparanoia fell ill between the ages of 40 and 54. Many were followed up into their sixties and seventies, and the full case-reports given demonstrate that they neither remitted nor demented. Interestingly, Kleist says in a footnote: "I suppose that some of these illnesses belong among those cases to which Kraepelin quite recently referred as paraphrenics" (present writer's translation). To return to Bleuler (1943), in addition to summarising the earlier literature, he also discussed his own material of 126 schizophrenics with onsets after the age of 40. Only 5 had fallen ill after 60, and the great majority had their first symptoms between 40 and 49. He admitted that this striking fall of first incidence after the age of 50 might not reflect a natural phenomenon, but might be the result of avoiding a schizophrenic diagnosis on account of undue preoccupation with so-called involutional features or of difficulties in excluding the presence of a senile psychosis. This suspicion seems to have been confirmed by a slightly later study. During a critical analysis of 355 case records of patients over the age of 65 admitted to the Heidelberg University Clinic between 1937 and 1948, Lechler (1950) allocated 30 cases to the schizophrenic category. Twelve had fallen ill before the age of 65, and most of them had suffered their first psychotic episodes between 40 and 50. In 10 of these patients with relatively early onsets, the case-record diagnosis had also been "schizophrenia", and only in 2 one of late life "dementia". By contrast, only 4 of the 18 patients first falling ill after the age of 65 had originally been labelled with what the author thought was the correct diagnosis; the remainder had been called "senile or arteriosclerotic paranoid illness", "involutional psychosis", or "dementia with hallucinations". Most, if not all, of the case histories quoted by Lechler, and also his finding (which agrees with that of other workers, e.g. Kay and Roth, 1961) that some 10 per cent of elderly persons admitted to psychiatric hospitals exhibited the schizophrenic reaction type in pure culture, suggest strongly that by-and-large he had been correct in his retrospective diagnoses. As we shall do in the present investigation, Lechler also stressed the frequency with which some depressive mood changes were present in these late schizophrenics. Many of the more recent investigations lack patients who, though labelled "late schizophrenia", started their illnesses during the senium. There are, for instance, studies of some 50 patients investigated at the Tuebingen University Clinic (Hirschmann and Klages, 1957; Klages, 1961). Only a few were over 60, and all had fallen ill before that age, but after 40. Christian Mueller (1959) is one of several authors who have investigated the effect of age changes in long-term schizophrenic hospital patients. Among his 101 cases, only 30 had been over the age of 40 at onset, and only 4 over the age of 60. In the most recent study of paranoid illnesses during the second half of life by Schimmelpenning (1965), the course of 82 patients was successfully followed over from 5 to 10 years. However, of the original 117 patients, only 9 had fallen ill after the age of 60, and the great majority (78) between 40 and 50. Patients were classified either as "late schizophrenics", exhibiting classical process symptoms and failing to recover, or as "schizoform" pursuing a chronic or a remitting course. Many of these episodic or periodic cases showed markedly depressive and anxious-agitated features. This author diagnosed from the case notes and also later during a personal follow-up examination in the great majority of patients one or the other organic psycho-syndrome (especially cerebral arteriosclerosis) as the basic illness, but few patients appeared to have progressed to a stage at which this disorder had become definitely incapacitating and irreversible.

Before we turn to investigations which at long last have begun to concern themselves primarily with patients becoming psychotic during the late involutional and senile periods, we should draw attention to another gap in our knowledge. What happens to people who, earlier in life, had shown paranoid tendencies which could not be classed as actual illnesses? As we shall see later in this report, many patients diagnosed in old age as late schizophrenics or paraphrenics had exhibited deviant, especially paranoid, personality traits earlier in life. In the absence of any forward-looking, long-term follow-through studies of paranoid personalities (which would be impossibly difficult to conduct) one can only surmise that many if not all of them end up as eccentric old people and senile recluses. However, no evidence has so far been produced to show whether and how often these senile character changes lead to persistent persecutory states demanding care and treatment (Post, 1965). On the contrary, surveys by general physicians and family doctors interested in geriatrics strongly suggest that these eccentric recluses do not suffer from truly psychotic symptoms (Sheldon, 1948; Miller, 1963). Against this, it may be objected that even experienced psychiatrists appear to have considerable difficulties in recognising the presence of paranoid mental illnesses during surveys of elderly people living in their own homes. Kay, Beamish and Roth (1964) failed to discover among 309 persons over 65 in Newcastle a single case to which they could attach Roth's label of "late paraphrenia". Only 3 women "exhibited strongly paranoid attitudes without other symptoms suggestive of schizophrenia. None of these cases was, so far as could be determined, hallucinated and none was so severely disturbed as to require urgent admission." Other recent domiciliary surveys have yielded similar results: only 4 paranoids among 228 elderly persons in a Welsh, and 2 among 200 in a Scottish study (Parsons, 1964; Williamson *et al.*, 1964). To judge from conversations with old people's welfare workers, one gains a strong impression that these figures represent considerable under-estimates, even allowing for the fact that in the Newcastle study 8 paraphrenic patients previously domiciled in the area from which the community sample had been drawn, were discovered in institutions or mental hospitals. There is a strong impression that especially in a family setting, paranoid disorders can smoulder on indefinitely underneath a conspiracy of silence. The writer has been told of an old man, whose relatives, even, did not realise that he had been mentally ill until after his death. Then they saw his diary, in which nothing but paranoid experiences had been recorded. But there are other circumstances in which it may remain impossible to decide when sensitive personality reactions have changed into an "illness", as the following example may illustrate.

Miss F., single and aged 64, had been a radiographer, who had had to retire 7 years earlier on account of an orthopaedic condition, complicated by compensation problems and the alleged presence of "functional overlay". For the last year, she had had to live in semi-institutional surroundings. She also did some voluntary work, and having attended a lecture given by the writer, she appealed to him for help: she felt that she had been given poor accommodation, next to an old lady who had driven a previous occupant away. She felt "the matron" was against her, and that the doctor who prescribed analgaesics and sedatives for her was unsympathetic. She was afraid she might become so distressed as to take an overdose: "I wonder whether I am going bonkers." On exploration, the patient was unhappy in a labile fashion, but not consistently depressed. Her accounts of various neglects, provocations and injustices sounded unlikely and exaggerated, but in no way bizarre or phantastic. The psychiatric social worker paid numerous visits to the patient and "the matron", seeing both separately, smoothing out scenes and outbursts as they arose, while over 18 months, the psychiatrist saw the patient supportively every few weeks. We came to the conclusion that here was a hypochondriacal, hypersensitive and emotionally labile woman, who craved for attention and who had stimulated considerable hostility by unreasonable demands and intemperate remarks. At the same time, we felt that our patient had not been well handled and was often provoked in a position of premature dependency, which she resented.

When on visits to relatives (too far away for us to get independent accounts of her previous adjustment), she felt much better, and it was hoped that transfer to different accommodation and greater independence might provide the answer to her problems. However, when the patient was at long last moved to a council flat, she immediately complained about noisy and interfering neighbours, and after the psychiatrist had shrugged his shoulders in desperation, she failed to keep her next appointment. She returned a year later, i.e. nearly 3 years after she had been originally seen. The other tenants wanted to get rid of her; they made a lot of noise, trampled on her portion of the garden, and peered into her windows. One of the women knew "the matron" and had been put wise. Even if she obtained another flat in the borough, "the matron" would see to it that her behaviour, or rather "the matron's" version of her behaviour, would become known in her new surroundings.

Among more recent studies concerning themselves with persistent paranoid conditions clearly requiring psychiatric care, there are several specificially related to patients who became psychotic for the first time after their sixtieth year. We shall once again refer to most of them when we come to discuss our own findings. At present, we shall only be concerned with rendering in outline the general results and thoughts of other investigators. Roth and Morrissey (1952), in their analysis of the records of 150 cases over 60 consecutively admitted to a regional mental hospital, diagnosed 2 men and 10 women as schizophrenics. "In each case the disorder had started after the age of 60 and was paraphrenic in character." Roth and Morrissey reminded their readers that paranoid delusions were regarded as part and parcel of a depressive illness when they were in harmony with the affective state, and could be interpreted as projections of ideas of guilt, unworthiness, and tendencies to self-castigation. Paranoid delusions could also be associated with senile psychoses (by which they meant the organic psychoses of old age). These seemed to arise out of the patients' failure of grasp and feeble contact with the environment. They were characteristically transient, non-systematised and ever-changing in character. In other words, these authors were particularly anxious to restrict the term "schizophrenic" to patients in whose case there were "paraphrenic delusions, which were prominent in each of the 12 cases. They occurred in each case in the setting of a well-preserved intellect and personality, were often 'primary' in character, and were usually associated with the passivity feelings or other volitional disturbances and hallucinations in clear consciousness, pathognomonic of schizophrenia." As regards outcome, only 3 patients had died during the 3 years following admission, 7 were still in hospital, and only 2 had been discharged. In a later study, Roth (1955) analysed the outcome of patients over 60 admitted to the same hospital at different times during the preceding 20 years. Among a total of 450 cases there were 12 men and 34 women with schizophrenic symptomatology, as defined above. Seventy-five per cent had first fallen ill after the age of 60, and with one exception, the illness had in all cases commenced after 45. At this stage Roth introduced the term of "late paraphrenia"—"because the clinical picture of most cases has many similarities to the paranoid illnesses described by Kraepelin under the heading of paraphrenia (later shown to be a relatively late form of schizophrenia)". Of 28 patients admitted in 1948 and 1949 and diagnosed as late paraphrenia on the basis of their case records, 7 were found to have been discharged 2 years after admission. Only 3 of 15 patients called late paraphrenics following personal examination during 1951 and 1952 left hospital. In 1957 Janzarik published a paper in which he reported his observations on 50 elderly schizophrenic patients. With a few exceptions, psychotic symptoms had first become manifest after the age of 60, the average age of onset being 67 and the latest age 79. To an even greater extent than in younger patients, illnesses hardly ever fitted one of the schizophrenic subgroups described in textbooks. Only 3 cases exhibited at some time or other catatonic features, and the same number pursued an insidious course, with a few paranoid symptoms only. Most illnesses were florid, often apparently precipitated by external events (very much in contrast with our own findings), and in 6 instances, the conditions remitted (length of follow-up not stated). Janzarik reported that patients tended to pass from one type of schizophrenic symptomatology to another, and that there was a trend for illnesses to start off with delusions (*Wahn*) in the foreground, but to turn increasingly into an hallucinosis. Of more immediate relevance to our own study was Janzarik's finding that there were often considerable difficulties in excluding diagnostically an affective illness with paranoid symptomatology. Moreover, patients tended to present with schizophrenic features at one time and with cyclothymic ones at another. This made him feel some regret at the passing into history of the unitary concept of psychosis (*Einheitspsychose*). In a study entitled "Senile schizophrenia", Fish (1960) competently summarised the earlier German literature, much as it has been presented here, and with special reference to the concept of paraphrenia. He criticised Roth for introducing the term "late paraphrenia", as German studies had shown that paraphrenics were simply paranoid schizophrenics of late onset. In any case, Kraepelin in the 1913 edition of his *Psychiatrie* had reported that 0·2 per cent of 1054 patients with dementia praecox (i.e. specifically excepting paraphrenia) had suffered their first attacks after the age of 60. In fact, it is quite clear that Roth (1955) was fully conversant with the dubious scientific status of the concept of paraphrenia (see p. 7 for quotation from his paper). In the present writer's opinion, the last words on this subject were spoken by Kolle (1931) and Mayer-Gross (1932, pp. 451–6), to the effect that attempts before, by and after Kraepelin to regard paranoia and paraphrenia as conditions with an aetiology, symptomatology and prognosis separate from paranoid schizophrenia had all failed, in the light of genetic and katamnestic studies. Making confusion worse confounded, Fish (1960) confirmed in a series of chronic schizophrenics that all those with onsets between 50 and 59 belonged to one of the subgroups of "paraphrenia" in terms of Leonhard's classification (Fish, 1958). He also investigated all patients over 60 admitted to psychiatric institutions from the City of Edinburgh. Among 41 with paranoid symptoms, there were 16 who satisfied his stringent criteria for the diagnosis of schizophrenia, but only 7 had fallen ill after 60. Again, all could be labelled as paraphrenics in Leonhard's sense (3, affect-laden; 2, phonemic; 1, hypochondriacal; 1, expansive). Three of these patients could be discharged, but Fish did not regard the follow-up (6–12 months) findings of this series as trustworthy. It will be seen that Fish agreed with Janzarik (1957) in finding that there was not just one typical clinical picture of senile schizophrenia.

By far the largest and most searching investigation of late life schizophrenia is the one reported by Kay and Roth (1961) and Kay (1963). They start off with a defence of the concept of late paraphrenia, claiming that the relationship between paraphrenic, paranoid, and schizophrenic illnesses has long been disputed, but that no view at present commanded general acceptance. They point out that some authorities look on chronic delusional states with or without hallucinations as mild forms of schizophrenia, attenuated and modified by certain constitutional features, while others regard paranoia and paranoid states as non-schizophrenic reactions. In Kay and Roth's investigation, no case of paranoid psychosis was excluded provided that signs of organic dementia or sustained confusion were absent, and that in terms of content, the delusional and hallucinatory symptoms were not due to a primary affective disorder. "Late paraphrenia" was simply used as a descriptive term. "In the result, cases were found to have more or less well-marked schizophrenic symptoms, and a small proportion exhibited no hallucinations. The material was studied as one group, in order to see what related factors emerged as the most significant and consistent. Different varieties would be identified if this proved possible and their aetiology studied." Thirty-nine women and two men were examined and investigated by the authors personally, in an English mental hospital. Most were successfully followed over at least 5 years. In addition, the records of 48 women and 9 men admitted to a Stockholm psychiatric teaching hospital were analysed, and the patients' courses were followed in most instances until death. The subjects in both series were over 60, and in none had the psychotic illness commenced before the age of 55. Certain features stood out in the background of most illnesses. In contrast to what has been found in schizophrenics at earlier ages, women predominated to a striking extent. There was a significant excess of unmarried persons. Paraphrenics had lived alone before admission significantly more often than elderly depressives, and an unduly large proportion had, domestic arrangements apart, been socially isolated. Like other workers, Kay and Roth found that elderly paraphrenics, as compared with depressives, tended to have good physical health, but to suffer from special sensory defects, especially deafness. Very much as in our own material (and again very much in contrast with the findings in depressives) few psychoses appeared to have been preceded, let alone precipitated, by traumatic events or physical illnesses. The duration of symptoms (as recorded) before admission was midway between that of depressives and senile dements. It depended more on the nature of the presenting symptoms, like aggressiveness or disturbance by hallucinations, and availability in the patients' social settings of reliable witnesses, than on the ultimate clinical picture. These were only briefly sketched in by the authors, mainly in order to demonstrate that the phenomena occurred in "clear consciousness" and had "a veritable schizophrenic quality". Attention is drawn to the relatively restricted and personal nature of delusional beliefs, but some 28 per cent experienced feelings of mental and physical influence. Most patients had hallucinations and in three-quarters, these were auditory in character. In some instances, the patient's thoughts were repeated aloud or messages received. Incoherence of speech and neologisms were very rare; verbosity and circumstantiality frequent, but possibly due to senility, though patients with serious cognitive defects had, as will be recalled, been excluded. In patients who had been ill for some time, there could perhaps be noted some affective changes: slight emotional blunting, mild incongruity, or euphoria. In a few patients, the final picture was difficult to distinguish from senile dementia, but the first incidence of definite organic cerebral disorders and the death rate of elderly paraphrenics were no different from that of the non-psychiatric elderly population.

We shall return to many of Kay and Roth's findings when we come to discuss our own, especially those relating to heredity, social factors, personality and treatment. At this stage, we shall only summarise a few points briefly. In keeping with the experiences of other workers, prognosis was regarded as unequivocally poor. Only 5 of 24 patients personally investigated and ascertained to be alive after 5 years were out of hospital, and only one could be said to have made a lasting recovery. In Sweden, more patients had been discharged under supervision, but about half spent the remainder of their lives in mental institutions. It was estimated that 57 individuals spent a combined total of nearly 600 years in hospital! An attempt by the authors to divide the material into three clinical varieties succeeded at a rather superficial level only. Twenty per cent of patients did not suffer any hallucinations; in 25 per cent the paraphrenias arose under unusual circumstances or after prolonged social isolation; and in 55 per cent the mental illness appeared at first sight to have been of largely endogenous origin. However, many features lost their significance on closer scrutiny, e.g. social isolation was often a result rather than a cause, and "reactive" cases had many "endogenous" schizophrenic features, like ideas of influence.

The first subvariety of patients without any hallucinosis formed perhaps a more homogeneous group. Compared with the rest, they were older, had more sensory defects due to ageing, their delusions were more prosaic, and the psychosis appeared more often to represent a direct continuation and caricature of the previous personality. In the long run, Kay and Roth discovered that all these distinctions became increasingly blurred after the illness had been present for a number of years, suggesting that all three had been of a qualitative rather than of a quantitative kind.

As mentioned earlier, these workers concluded that late paraphrenia should be regarded as the mode of manifestation of schizophrenia in old age. "The aetiological factors identified in late paraphrenia are therefore likely to have some relevance for the problem of causation of schizophrenia itself. . . ." We shall return to this point in our last chapter.

CHAPTER 2

Aims and Method of Investigation

Publications which form the background of the present study have, as we saw, been largely concerned with phaenemonology and aetiology of paranoid disorders in elderly people. Most of them were based on an analysis of case records, but usually the patients had been examined by the investigators at one stage or other of the illness. Over the last 50 years, it has become gradually accepted that persistent paranoid psychoses can arise for the first time quite late in life, in the absence of senile or arteriosclerotic dementia, and that their symptoms were indistinguishable from those seen at an earlier age in paranoid schizophrenics. By contrast, hebephrenic or catatonic pictures hardly ever appeared for the first time during late adult life. Most illnesses were characterised by paranoid delusions and usually also by hallucinations in all sensory modalities. There was general agreement to the effect that true incongruity of affect and schizophrenic disorders of formal thinking developed only rarely and were, on account of their mildness, difficult to differentiate from the effects of senility and institutionalisation. Descriptively, these conditions thus would appear to fit into Kraepelin's group of "paraphrenics", a term which was later shown to have descriptive, but not aetiological or prognostic significance. One cannot imagine that the continued use of this label, its reinstitution as late paraphrenia, or controversies concerning this matter are likely to further our understanding of schizophrenia as seen in late life.

Patients with this late illness show far less dilapidations of personality than subjects with earlier onsets. They usually maintain a better social adjustment, and more frequently remain able to live outside mental institutions. All the same, recoveries or lasting remissions have in the past been regarded as most unusual. There are, however, a few exceptions. Thus, Klages (1961) reported that following insulin comas, electroconvulsive therapy (ECT), or continuous sleep, 33 patients in his series recovered fully within a few weeks or months and that they remained over many years as they had been before the illness. Nine subjects showed slight permanent, and another nine more severe defects, with only six having to remain in hospital permanently. All his patients had fallen ill between the ages of 40 and 60, and were thus younger than most cases discussed by other writers on late or senile schizophrenia. The therapeutic results achieved at this author's clinic (Tuebingen) were surprisingly good, but it should be pointed out that according to Klages' reports, there were many patients who had exhibited marked depressive features, suicidal behaviour, and acute onsets following traumatic events. They were regarded as schizophrenics, because the depressive features never became the leading ones, as according to Klages always occurred in cases of mixed psychoses. All the same, one wonders whether many patients were not of the kind excluded in the present and other studies as melancholics with paranoid, or even with a few non-pathognomic schizophrenic symptoms. In any case, full remissions lasting for many years in 33 out of 51 schizo-affectives or melancholics with paranoid symptoms falling ill for the first time during the involutional period of life must be regarded as very unusual. Another worker (Sheps, 1958) has claimed good results with social measures, including relationship therapy. However, many of his cases were suffering from basically psycho-organic conditions, in which the variability and transitory nature of paranoid symptoms has to be remembered. The same objection holds in the case of Davidson (1964) who suggested that in the management of paranoid disorders social measures were most important, and that medication played only an adjuvant role.

All other writers are unequivocally pessimistic concerning immediate and especially long-term response to any form of treatment. Quite recently, Haase (1963) discussed the poor results obtained with social and psychological treatments in paranoid and paranoid-hallucinatory disorders of ageing women living alone. Kay and Roth (1961) confirmed that ECT or tranquillising drugs ("which appeared to be of value in disturbed cases") produced remissions in about one-quarter of late paraphrenics treated in an English mental hospital. Sometimes, these remissions had lasted several months, but in spite of further courses of treatment only one patient had finally remained well, possibly on account of a favourable change in her social circumstances. Janzarik (1957) also mentions that ECT and medications can produce temporary remissions. Interestingly, he quotes among his clinical examples the case of a woman of 77 whose paranoid-hallucinatory illness responded twice to courses of chlorpromazine, relapsing on each occasion after a few months, and finally requiring long-term hospitalisation. The possibility of maintenance drug therapy is not mentioned. Perhaps with prophetic insight, the husband of one of Fish's (1960) discharged patients with "hypochondriacal paraphrenia" attributed his wife's continued good progress to the chlorpromazine which she was still taking. However, Fish felt that this man was an unreliable witness.

Like other psychiatrists, the present writer began to introduce occasionally some ten years ago, one or the other of the so-called ataractic, neuroleptic, psychotropic, or tranquillising drugs used in younger schizophrenics, into the management of elderly patients whose paranoid symptoms were not apparently secondary to an affective or organic psychosis. It will presently be seen that the investigations reported in this monograph succeeded in confirming earlier impressions that treatment with some phenothiazine-type, tranquillising preparations given in sufficiently large amounts was followed by the disappearance or considerable attenuation of paranoid preoccupations, delusions, hallucinations, and even of classical paranoid-schizophrenic symptoms first arising during late life. It will be shown that, under certain circumstances, the use of these drugs can lead to a striking improvement in the long-term outcome of the paranoid disorders of old age. Though not contributing towards a better understanding of the basic causes of schizophrenia, the findings of this clinically orientated study are thought to lend support to an hypothesis according to which schizophrenic ways of experiencing, feeling, thinking and acting are latently present in many, possibly all, members of the human species, and this investigation of elderly paranoid patients has supplied some explanations for the causation and symptomatology of schizophrenic or schizophrenia-like phenomena, manifesting themselves in varying circumstances and during different periods of life.

In an earlier follow-up study of 100 elderly patients with affective illnesses, index admissions and initial treatment had been spread over only 18 months (Post, 1962). Paranoid illnesses are much rarer; probably they form only 8–10 per cent of all new admissions to mental hospitals over the age of 65 (Kay and Roth, 1961). For this reason, almost 10 years had passed before it was possible to look back on a series of elderly paranoid patients, comparable with the previously studied sample of depressives in size and length of observation period. The present report is based on a consecutive sample of patients coming under the writer's care since late in 1954. All those patients (93) were included, who had been followed for at least one year; in all but the most recently admitted patients, the follow-up date was fixed as 36 months after beginning of treatment. In many, the observation period extended over a longer span of time, but later developments were not registered for analysis of the data. Any study extending over so many years inevitably suffers from a number of methodological flaws.

First and foremost, there have been important changes in the treatment and management of patients with schizophrenic illnesses. Up to 1959, elderly patients with paranoid symptoms not secondary to a transitional organic confusional state were regarded as incurable cases. The best that could be hoped for was encapsulation of symptoms or their acceptance by the patient's entourage. Occasionally, manipulation of the patient's social circumstances, e.g. change of home, appeared successful, but tranquillising drugs were administered to elderly paranoid patients only half-heartedly and with little confidence in their efficacy. We saw that these pessimistic views were aired by Kay and Roth as late as 1961, and by Davidson (1964) in a modified form even more recently. However, by 1959 occasional results with adequate phenothiazine treatment were sufficiently impressive to encourage fuller investigation. In September 1959 a controlled trial of trifluoperazine (Stelazine) was started at the geriatric unit of the Bethlem Royal Hospital in co-operation with Dr. Hugh Freeman (then working at the unit), who had drafted the following plan: without knowledge of the doctors or nurses and in accordance with a randomisation schedule, subjects were to be given during 12 weeks either first the drug and then a placebo (kindly supplied by Messrs. Smith, Kline & French), or vice versa. Dosages were worked up if necessary to 30 mg daily, and anti-parkinsonian drugs were given as indicated. However, this trial ran into difficulties, on account of a low admission rate, staff changes, and a prolonged illness of the author's, which interfered with the administration of a projected elaborate rating system. All the same, a preliminary analysis (Post, 1962a) demonstrated that not a single patient had lost his symptoms while on a placebo, and that most patients had responded favourably to trifluoperazine. By then, there were only a few psychiatrists who seriously doubted that many phenothiazines and other psychotropic preparations removed or suppressed various symptoms belonging to the schizophrenic mental reaction type, and interest shifted towards the long-term effectiveness of this treatment. All patients with non-affective paranoid symptoms passing through the geriatric unit between 1954 and February 1961 were followed up, and their course determined for 36 months following their index admission.

TABLE 1. DIFFERENCES OF INTENSITY OF PERSONAL CONTACT AND DRUG THERAPY IN THREE CONSECUTIVE SAMPLES OF PARANOID PATIENTS

	First series	Second series	Third series	Total
Number of patients	24	37	32	93
Follow-through				
By investigator throughout	3	29	20*	52
Initially by investigator, later by PSW and other reports	8	7	9	24
PSW and medical reports, only source of information	13	1	—	14
Phenothiazine therapy				
None or inadequate	20	—	2	22
Adequate but not maintained	4†	12	12	28
Adequate and fully maintained	—	25	18	43

*Three patients attended the writer once or twice, but were then irretrievably lost.

†These patients were given full courses of phenothiazines later during the follow-up period, mainly by other psychiatrists.

All patients treated subsequent to February 1961 were also followed, and were included for study if at the time of the analysis of data, at least one year had elapsed since the start of treatment.

The total research sample of 93 patients is thus made up of three consecutive series, given in detail in Table 1. The first series was admitted between the end of 1954 and August 1959; 20 of these 24 patients had at no time adequate phenothiazine therapy, but 4 received this type of treatment at a later stage of the observation period, usually from psychiatrists other than the author. The second series consisted of 37 patients admitted between September 1959 and February 1961; all these had initially received adequate courses of a phenothiazine drug, but long-term maintenance had failed in 12 instances. Both these earlier series were followed over 3 years (unless, of course, death occurred earlier); 32 patients, forming the third series, were admitted to treatment starting in March 1961. All except 2 patients defaulting early received full courses of drugs initially, but only 18 had successful maintenance treatment. Length and method of follow-up of members of this third series are recorded in Table 10 (p. 41).

These three samples, collected over 10 years, differed in respects other than drug therapy. The follow-up of members of the first series was a retrospective one, and only a few patients were again seen by the writer personally (see Table 1). Patients had been admitted more often from a mental observation ward than was the case with members of the later series, largely to clarify diagnosis. If the presence of a basically affective or remediable psycho-organic disorder could be excluded, they were regarded as incurable, and if necessary, referred immediately or at a later date to psychiatrists with long-stay beds at their disposal. By contrast, after 1959 as many patients as possible were admitted, as long as they exhibited a paranoid and/or schizophrenic symptomatology, and for this reason members of the second series were more often suffering from organic mental syndromes. On the other hand, in comparison with the first sample, they were slightly younger, and slightly less often widowed or socially isolated. Strenuous efforts were made to keep these patients under personal supervision and to maintain their drug therapy. Members of the third series were treated at a time when the efficacy of phenothiazine therapy seemed established, and, whenever feasible, treatment was attempted in the outpatient clinic (13 out of 32 patients, only 2 of whom required admission later). Staff shortage made enforcement of maintenance therapy by a psychiatric social worker not always possible in this third phase of the study, and after failing repeatedly-offered appointments, some patients were only contacted again for follow-up rather than for therapeutic purposes.

When comparing the results achieved with these three consecutive series of patients, the differences referred to between the three samples will have to be taken into consideration. In an investigation where the ground was continually shifting, because data had to be gathered over nearly 10 years, the presence or absence of drug therapy were not the only important variables. For this reason statistical tests will only be applied to some of the suspected trends because either numbers in each phase were too small, or the groups not strictly comparable.

CHAPTER 3

Clinical Characteristics of Patients

All patients were over 60 and were suffering for the first time in life after the age of 50 from paranoid symptoms unrelated to an affective illness. Patients who had at first been regarded as schizophrenic or paraphrenic, but who after treatment and follow-up appeared to have been manics or melancholics, were excluded from this study. This, and especially failure to record these cases proved unfortunate, as the relationship between affective and schizophrenic disturbances among the elderly may be of great interest, from a practical as well as from a theoretical angle. A retrospective study of "schizo-affective" cases was not possible, as we had only registered those who turned out to be schizophrenic, but a forward-looking investigation has now been started. Included in the present study were patients presenting with persistent paranoid symptomatology on the background of proved or strongly suspected pathological changes in the brain.

Organic brain damage was confirmed (by outcome or post-mortem (P.M.)) in 16 of 93 patients, and was still regarded as doubtfully present at follow-up in 17. Restricting ourselves to the 61 patients of the first two samples, who were followed for 3 years (unless, of course, death had occurred earlier) the diagnosis of "organic paranoid state" had been made in 17 on admission, and was confirmed in 13, with 4 patients moving into the "doubtfully organic" category. This change of category was suggested by the further outcome of 3 (none of them followed up personally) and by a negative macroscopic and microscopic neuropathologist's report in the fourth patient. As has been pointed out in the past (Post, 1962, 1965) the mere suspicion of brain damage and dementia in mentally disordered elderly persons is only rarely confirmed on follow-up, in fact only once in 18 of these paranoid patients followed over 3 years (cerebrovascular accident while in another hospital, reliable clinical account, but no P.M.). Only 2 patients originally classed as free of brain damage developed mild cognitive disabilities, and no patient in this category showed definite organic cerebral disease or deterioration. Diagnostically, the 16 patients with confirmed organic psychoses fell into the categories listed in Table 2. Diagnoses were confirmed by exhaustive pathological investigations in only 5 instances.

TABLE 2. DIAGNOSTIC BREAKDOWN OF PATIENTS WITH CONFIRMED CEREBRAL DISORDERS.
(All three samples.)

Predominantly senile dementia	5
Predominantly arteriosclerotic dementia	7
Pre-senile dementia Alzheimer	1
Pre-senile dementia Jacob–Creutzfeld (P.M.)	1
Neurosyphilis atypical G.P.I.	1
Symptomatic epilepsy due to cerebral thrombophelebitis	1
	16

Disordered thought content mainly took the form of delusions of persecution, which were present in all but one patient:

Mrs. E.W., *aet.* 64, believed that her husband gave off a peculiar odour because he took drugs. Not she, but he needed treatment. Further exploration of this delusion (or hallucination?) failed. Three years later, the patient's husband continued to be distressed by the patient's incessant accusations, but as there were no other symptoms, he could never again bring himself to ask for her admission to an observation ward.

None of the patients in this series was admitted only because he entertained delusional beliefs which were based on some experience in the past. Their beliefs were always associated with other ongoing psychotic symptoms. A few patients had grandiose ideas, and depressive preoccupations and delusions were almost as frequent as depressive mood disturbances, a subject to which we shall return presently.

Hallucinosis. This did not differ in kind from the usual textbook descriptions, and was mostly auditory in type; touch, taste, and smell hallucinations occurred much more rarely. In 10 patients, no hallucinations were discovered throughout the observation period, but (as in the case just quoted) it was sometimes difficult to decide whether the sources of delusional beliefs were not perhaps hallucinatory in type. One patient felt that her dead parents were in communication with her by hypnosis, but she never admitted to receiving any verbal messages. Another remained convinced that his wife (apart from being unfaithful) was putting croton oil in his food (he had been a mental attendant many years ago). Yet another patient was nicknamed Electricity Jane in the institution from which she came, because she complained that electricity was directed to her legs.

"*Schizophreniform*" *symptoms*. Both this word and, in contrast with it, "schizophrenic", are used in this report with greatest reluctance and only in order to avoid having to coin some new terms. The underlying concepts of process or nuclear schizophrenia, of atypical schizophrenia, of symptomatic schizophrenia, etc. are regarded by this writer as premature and unsatisfactory attempts at coming to grips with the riddle of schizophrenia. "Schizophrenic" and "schizophreniform" are used here in a narrowly defined, special sense. In this study, all pathological phenomena are called "schizophreniform" as long as they are *understandable* without recourse to psychoanalytical concepts or to other systems of depth-psychopathology, and while making generous allowance for the patient's cultural background and intelligence. There seems little point in enumerating and comparing the frequency of many often-described symptoms. Ideas of theft were especially common in this elderly sample and they also took the form of convictions that false money had been planted on the patient, or that electricity, gas or water supplies were interfered with. Ideas of poisoning often extended to preoccupations with unpleasant smells and to beliefs that gases were pumped into the patient's room. Others believed that they were being observed by some form of apparatus, that photographs were being taken in embarrassing circumstances, or that lights were being directed towards them. They might believe that their rooms were wired and conversations were recorded. Klages (1961) pointed out that in his late (onsets 40–60 years) schizophrenics, delusional themes tended to be much more concrete and earthbound than those seen in younger patients, and he thought that this presented a transition stage to the banality shown in the paranoid ideas of senile dements. He was probably referring to what we have termed "schizophreniform" phenomena. However, ecstatic and "out of this world" experiences do also occur in senile paranoid patients.

"*Schizophrenic*" was a label attached only to patients with Kurt Schneider's (1959 translation) symptoms of first-rank for making a diagnosis of schizophrenia. Many of these symptoms are not seen in elderly patients, but the following phenomena were classed as "schizophrenic": feelings of guidance, trance or hypnosis; intrusions or withdrawals of thoughts; stabs and shocks entering the patient from outside; bizarre changes in the patient's surroundings (e.g. persons continually changing in size due to some mental action by the patient); furthermore, phantastic experiences and beliefs, like involvement in a German (1961 !) plot, seeing bodies carried out of the house, levitation (by police action), taking part in a television programme within a complex hallucinosis, intimate conversations with an apparition of the "Archangel Michael" and also with the "Heavenly Father". Finally, auditory hallucinations were called "schizophrenic" only when they repeated or anticipated the patient's thoughts, gave a running commentary on his actions, or discussed him in the third person singular. It must be admitted that (contrary to the claim advanced by Schneider) a clear differentiation between "schizophrenic" and "schizophreniform" was sometimes difficult, and some patients presented both types of phenomena. However, similar diagnostic criteria have been employed by Scandinavian workers (perhaps most explicitly stated by Astrup, Fossum and Holmboe, 1962). Though many of our patients had been ill for several years, none seemed to fit very well into the categories of the Leonhard classification (as expounded by Fish, 1958). Possibly, some "schizophreniform" cases corresponded to the affect-laden paraphrenias, and some "schizophrenic" ones to the phonemic paraphrenias and hypochondriacal paraphrenias, all three clinical entities accounting for all but one of Fish's (1960) senile schizophrenics. First-rank symptoms, like fragmentation of thinking processes, cataplexy, manneristic and stereotyped movements, were never recognised with any degree of certainty, nor was true incongruity of affect ever noted. The "Praecox-gefuehl" is rare even in chronic schizophrenics examined during old age (Ruemke, 1963). However, a proportion of patients seemed unable to communicate their affective state clearly and appropriately, and they usually showed marked perplexity as well.

Affective symptoms were most frequently those of depression. They occurred in 53 of 93 patients; in 20 the depressive features were at times severe and dominating the clinical picture. Anxiety, which was always clearly related to persecutory experiences, was almost equally often present. Elation was more rarely encountered, and almost always in patients who at other times showed depression or anxiety. Many patients with depressive mood changes felt themselves persecuted from a position of inferiority, felt unattractive, poverty-stricken, might even blame themselves and express ideas of guilt. They were not excluded as melancholics, because they also exhibited symptoms belonging to the schizophrenic reaction type. Using the term in our special and restricted sense, "schizophrenic" symptoms were least often encountered in patients with well-marked depressive admixtures, but this negative association was far from statistically significant. By contrast, poor communication of affect was noted outstandingly often in "schizophrenic" patients, but on account of the subjective nature of this judgement and the inconspicuousness of this abnormality, statistical tests seemed inappropriate.

The distribution and interrelation of all these clinical characteristics will be found in Table 3, and will now be discussed further.

TABLE 3. RELATIONSHIP BETWEEN A NUMBER OF CLINICAL CHARACTERISTICS

	Hallucinosis only	"Schizo-phreniform" symptoms present	Some "schi-zophrenic" phenomena noted	Total
Number of patients	22	37	34	93
Depression				
Severe	5	9	6	20
Mild	8	14	11	33
Poor communication of affect	1	5	16	22
Deafness present	9	10	9	28
Organic cerebral changes				
Confirmed on follow-up	6	6	4	16
Still suspected	4	8	5	17

CHAPTER 4

Three Clinical Syndromes

Only about one-third of this sample of paranoid elderly patients (34 of 93) were found to be suffering from symptoms classified as "schizophrenic" for the purpose of this investigation. They heard voices which commented on their activities, discussed the patients in the third person, or echoed their thoughts; they had passivity and other experiences interpreted as dissolution of ego boundaries, or held bizarre and phantastic beliefs. These patients appeared to be suffering from a separate "*schizophrenic*" *syndrome*, though two-thirds of their number exhibited some "schizophreniform" symptoms as well. These occurred without any "schizophrenic" features in 37 patients and, as described on p. 21, took the form of paranoid experiences of a more understandable type: seeing policemen watching them, rooms being wired, microphones hidden, smells and gases directed at them, photographs taken, etc. These patients were provisionally allocated to a "*schizophreniform*" *syndrome*. We saw (p. 20) that almost all patients were hallucinated at some stage, but there was a group of 22 who experienced (almost always auditory) hallucinations without any "schizophreniform" or "schizophrenic" symptoms. They held paranoid beliefs, but these were solely based on, or confirmed by, their pathological perceptions. These patients were placed in a third syndrome, which we will call "*paranoid hallucinosis*".

A few case summaries will be given, illustrating the characteristics of these three syndromes, while at the same time submitting to the reader's scrutiny some of the differentiating features employed. Paranoid hallucinosis in its simplest form occurring in a deaf person will be presented in a case report (Miss S. W.) on p. 28. A more complex clinical picture will be given here.

Mrs. A. M. had an identical twin who, like the rest of the family, appeared to be mentally normal, except for striking a somewhat paranoid attitude when asked to co-operate once again in further twin-investigations. The patient had been a cheerful laundry worker, whose first husband was killed in World War I. She soon remarried, both marriages were happy and blessed with 4 children. She was a friendly and sociable member of a closely knit Cockney family.

Aet. 63, the patient began to have occasional preoccupations with her stomach and feelings of exhaustion. *Aet.* 65, she started to complain that she heard neighbours saying she was responsible for the loss of a pension book, and that she was dirty. This, with poor sleep, restlessness, and tearfulness, led to her admission under the writer's care. During 2 months in hospital, all symptoms remitted without any special treatment. The only physical abnormality was some arterial hypertension, of exactly the same degree as that found in the identical twin. A diagnosis of a mild depressive reaction with paranoid features, possibly related to early cerebral arterio-sclerosis, was made. Within one month of discharge all symptoms recurred, but appeared to remit after five electroconvulsive treatments.

The patient was followed for the subsequent 18 months, during which time she continued to suffer from occasional, socially not disturbing paranoid episodes, but no deterioration from her low average level of intelligence was observed. At the age of 76, she was referred back as an out-patient. Her daughter confirmed that the patient had continued to feel during the intervening 8 years that people were talking about her, but that until 6 weeks ago this had not led to any obvious disturbances. However, recently, her mother had again become agitated and continually complained of hearing voices accusing her of being dirty and also informing her of an impending raid on her wardrobe. Sometimes she would smile; at others she would shout back at the voices.

By now the patient had turned slightly deaf, but there was no increase of hyper-tension or decrease of mental abilities. Depression was in no way obvious, and ex-periences of influence or passivity were denied. In fact, her symptomatology was limited to concern with the voices of "thieves", talking from downstairs in obscene and uncomplimentary terms. There was a rapid and complete response to thioridazine therapy as an out-patient. After 10 months, this was discontinued. Six weeks later auditory hallucinosis, agitation and sleeplessness returned, only to disappear again 2 weeks after resuming thioridazine.

Our next example is of an intractible schizophreniform psychosis.

Mrs. M. V., a widow *aet.* 76, without family history of psychiatric disorder, held semi-skilled positions until her marriage at the age of 40 to a somewhat younger man, who died 30 years later in a mental hospital. His illness had probably been a paranoid depression. The marriage had been childless, and intercourse rare and not enjoyable.

There was a suggestion that she married at a time when she was mildly depressed following her mother's death; she was similarly depressed, but again not requiring psychiatric treatment following her husband's demise. She had been living alone, visiting relatives and superficially on good terms with neighbours who regarded her as stand-offish, snobbish and somewhat eccentric. Her flat was situated in a tenement house on the borders of Soho (one of the entertainment areas in the West End of London).

The patient was admitted to a mental observation ward after disturbances, con-tinuing intermittently over 3 days. She had roused a neighbour in the middle of the night, had appeared very frightened and upset, declaring that a searchlight was being directed into her room, and that she was being watched by 2 men from the house opposite. She also reported to the police that she had seen a man with a torch. In hospital, where she was found to be physically normal, of low average intelligence and without any evidence of alcoholism, she described her symptoms more fully, in retrospect: "As I was in bed, I saw a torch in my room—a light—trying to find me on the bed. . . . They were three vertical bars in red. . . . Out of the window I saw something like a balloon flying up yellow, not the sun or the moon, it frightened me." At a later stage, she described a balloon following her on a visit to her sister in the country; on another occasion, she said that a large syringe had been attached to the balloon. All these experiences had ceased since her admission and did not return on her transfer to our unit. She had never heard any voices or noises, and did not feel herself hypnotized or interfered with in any physical or mental way. In retrospect, her experiences puzzled her, and she admitted that some new neon lights on a nearby theatre might have played on her imagination.

Her condition was provisionally labelled "paranoid state", but one senior colleague thought in terms of an hysterical reaction with ill-concealed sexual content, occurring in a lonely woman. However, one month following discharge, the patient had to be readmitted: she felt a torch was shining into her eyes, and that people from downstairs were spraying her to punish her for having seen (before her first admission) what she ought not to have seen(!). Once again, all active symptoms cleared on admission, but all the same she was placed on trifluoperazine.

The patient was followed over more than 3 years, during which time she remained mentally unwell, except during two further admissions. Her hallucinations were probably controlled by phenothiazines and returned when they were omitted. But all the time she remained very frightened, would not stay in her flat during the day, and would barricade herself at night. She was frequently distressed and tearful, complaining that the sun and moon followed her about everywhere. Attempts at resettling her in a home for the elderly were at first resisted by the patient, and later proved unsuccessful.

Finally, the record of a patient who presented the classical paranoid schizophrenic type of clinical picture, including an autochtonous delusion.

Mrs. J. W., a widow *aet.* 61, without any family history of psychiatric disorder. Before marriage and after becoming a widow at the age of 45, she had worked in various domestic employments, and had been a popular and sociable person, who was not in general suspicious or over-sensitive. Her marriage had probably been sexually unsatisfactory—only one son, according to whom she had often accused her husband, rightly or wrongly, of infidelity.

One year before admission, the patient had moved from the country to a flat near her son. The only abnormality noted at that time was that she spoke embarrassingly openly about sexual matters. One month before admission, her daughter-in-law received a letter from the patient, in which she alleged a number of persecutions and also that a man was hypnotising her and making her a "martyr". One week before admission, the patient attacked a young girl in the street and was taken to a police station where she seemed incoherent, unsuitably jocular, and betrayed the fact that she heard imaginary voices.

Physically, there was no abnormality, and she looked if anything younger than her age. She gave a fairly coherent account of her recent experiences. She alleged that following her husband's death, she had had a number of physically satisfactory love affairs; finally, some years ago, she had been jilted (at first she said he had died) by a man whom she had wanted to marry. Three years ago, on return to the family home in the country (the affair had led her to live abroad), she began to overhear remarks as if between several persons, not only containing orders to herself, but also comments on her every action in the form of conversations. After 2 years she fled to London, but she soon developed a feeling that "searing needles" were being pushed through the back of her head. Some months before admission, she had seen a man in the street and was immediately and unshakably sure that he was the young soldier who had momentarily passed her window during the First World War, when she was a girl of 17. She began to feel that he was hypnotising her with sexual intent, and that he produced inside her partly pleasant, and partly disgusting sensations of coitus. The commenting voices continued, and led to the assault of a complete stranger. A slight discrepancy was noted between the unpleasant nature of the patient's experiences and the bland, and smiling way in which she related them.

All symptoms rapidly ceased on a daily 10 mg of trifluoperazine. Medication was stopped while the patient was still in hospital, but resumed after she reported that feathers were stroking her head, that she could feel and hear them, and that these sensations were produced by God as a reward for faith. This patient has now been followed for more than 2 years. On account of parkinsonism and depressive anergia, she was changed over to thioridazine. After one year, this was discontinued, but within 2 weeks she began to feel "tense and nervous", and to hear a male voice calling her surname. Since then she has remained symptom-free on 75 mg daily, visiting friends, her church, and the public house for a social drink. Once or twice she tried to leave off her thioridazine, but after a day or two she begins to feel nervous. "I am sure it all was a mental disturbance. What else could it be?"

Our three subsyndromes were derived from an analysis of symptoms of the first two samples of patients, but the same kind of clustering of symptoms was observed in the third sample, and in similar proportions. There thus seemed to exist a possibility that these descriptive differences within a group of elderly paranoid patients might be of some more fundamental significance as far as aetiology, and perhaps response to treatment and prognosis were concerned. Members of the "schizophrenic syndrome" were clearly the kind of patients in whose case psychiatrists of all schools and all nationalities would make a diagnosis of paranoid schizophrenia or of paraphrenia. Many might refuse to attach these labels to our "schizophreniform" and paranoid hallucinosis patients. It could be argued that the occurrence of "schizophrenic" symptoms gave the illnesses a more endogenous and constitutional flavour, while the psychodynamically more comprehensible "schizophreniform" symptomatology presented a reaction similar to an hysterical one, as in the case of Mrs. M. V. just quoted. Finally, the overhearing of voices and other noises, which were the sole basic symptoms in subjects with a "paranoid hallucinosis", might be most easily understood as exaggerations and misinterpretations by old people, perhaps living alone and suffering from sensory handicaps.

Deafness and paranoid symptoms have a long-standing and frequently confirmed association (see also Houston and Royse, 1954). It was found to have been present in 30 per cent of our cases (one patient was blind, as well), a proportion very similar to that given by Kay and Roth (1961). In marked contrast, deafness occurred in only 11 per cent of elderly depressives (1962), a figure not much higher than that given (7 per cent) for old people living in the community (Kay, Beamish and Roth, 1964). However, deafness was only slightly more often encountered in the most easily understandable paranoid illness, hallucinosis, as compared with its prevalence in the other two syndromes (not beyond chance expectation; Table 3). There was in fact only one patient who exhibited the classical hallucinosis of the deaf.

Miss S. W., *aet.* 76, who was described as a confirmed spinster, had after many years of increasing deafness begun to hear "light music", and had at first found this an amusing experience, due to "my ears". Much more recently, there supervened frightening and unpleasant voices, which finally commanded her to walk in the middle of the night from her lonely home (? wish-fulfilling mechanism) to her niece's house many miles away.

Physical health and brain damage. In comparison with elderly depressives, whose illnesses are so often precipitated by physical causes, paranoid old people tend to be sturdy and healthy, and the patients in this study proved no exception. All were observed for at least one year, and 64 of 93 for at least 3 years. Only 15 patients were known to have died, and only 2 of them (both dying in the third year of the follow-up period) had been regarded as definitely free of cerebral changes. Causes of death are recorded in Table 4. All patients with suspected or confirmed cerebral pathology suffered from paranoid symptoms which were not just the temporary and fleeting features of a confusional state, and which were indistinguishable in form and content from those seen in patients with intact brains (as witnessed by neurological and cognitive status, as well as follow-up findings). Like them, they presented with "schizophrenic", "schizophreniform" or paranoid hallucinosis syndromes, and the slight differences in the proportions shown in Table 3 were statistically insignificant. No support was, therefore,

TABLE 4. FREQUENCY AND CAUSES OF DEATH RELATED TO THE CLINICAL DIAGNOSIS OF BRAIN DAMAGE

Causes of death	Psychiatric diagnosis			
	"Organic"	Doubtfully "organic"	"Functional"	Total
Cerebral arteriosclerosis (Hosp. report or P.M.)	4	—	—	4
Cerebral arteriosclerosis (family doctor)	—	1	—	1
Jacob–Creutzfeld disease	1	—	—	1
Intestinal obstruction and brain damage	1	—	—	1
Bronchopneumonia	1	1	1	3
Cardiac degeneration	1	2	—	3
Coal-gas (? accident, ? suicide)	—	1	—	1
Street accident (very deaf)	—	—	1	1
	8	5	2	15

found for the existence of a specifically organic or "symptomatic" chronic paranoid psychosis, just as we had been unable to find evidence for the existence of the concept of organic depression (1962). We shall also be able to show that results of therapy and general outlook did not differ in organic, as compared with functional paranoid patients, apart from the ill-effects produced by brain damage on health, further duration of life, and social adjustment. In the earlier study (1962, Chapter VI) 38 out of 96 depressives exhibited definite cerebral-arteriosclerotic or senile changes during an observation period of 8 years, and this accumulative incidence was not regarded as in excess of what might be found in the non-depressive elderly population. During a much shorter period at risk, 93 paranoid patients produced only 16 with cerebral lesions, a proportion of an order similar to that seen in elderly depressives. In their case, it had been concluded that the occurrence of both depressive and cerebral-organic symptoms in the same patient were probably coincidental, though strikingly temporal sequences of depressions following strokes suggested a mechanism of precipitation in some instances. Many depressive patients with brain damage had suffered affective illnesses earlier in life. Evidence of paranoid symptoms having been acutely triggered off by pathological cerebral events was only rarely discovered in this sample, and the aetiological role of brain changes in promoting a schizophrenic type of reaction in elderly patients is even more uncertain than in depressives. We shall return to this matter (pp. 78–83).

Additional aetiological factors were conspicuous by their doubtful significance, and many special characteristics of these patients in the areas of their previous personalities, their social status and their adjustment, might well have been the forerunners rather than the cause of their psychoses. These features were often important prognostic factors mainly, as we shall see, by promoting or hindering long-term management, and will therefore be left to a later section. At present, we shall only consider emotional, constitutional and hereditary causal factors.

In some 60 per cent of elderly depressives, their illness had been preceded by some outstanding emotional stress or event, almost always representing some sort of loss or threat of loss. By contrast, it was not possible to relate the onset of paranoid symptoms to some definite and outstanding event, except very rarely to the death of a spouse. Even then, and when the patient's friends reported that the symptoms had come on suddenly, closer enquiry usually revealed that unvoiced paranoid preoccupations had been present for a long time. In one case—to give an example—it became quite clear that the patient had been participating for several years in a *folie à deux* with her husband, to whose death her illness had been originally attributed.

Environmental factors came to be strongly suspected in a sizeable proportion of patients whose psychotic symptoms underwent a striking change for the better each time they were admitted to hospital, or in some instances during stays with friends. Omitting patients in whom this change evaporated after a few weeks, persistent topical limitation of symptoms occurred in 20 of 61 patients of the first two samples, and in 9 of the third series of 32 patients. This slightly lower incidence was probably related to the fact that many of these more recent patients had ambulant treatment, when there was less chance of observing the effect of environmental change. Patients remained convinced of the reality of their past experiences, and continued to believe that their persecutors would resume their activities as soon as they returned home, but while away from their home surroundings, they did not experience any hallucinations or other psychotic experiences which one could call "active". Against expectation, patients whose symptoms were modified by changes in the environment did not differ from the rest in any social variables, e.g. only 12 of 29 had been living alone, almost exactly the same proportion as in the total sample. There was, however, one remarkable finding, to which we shall return later. Whereas environmental changes removed "active" psychotic symptoms in similar proportions of patients with either a paranoid hallucinosis or a "schizophreniform" syndrome, not a single patient with a "schizophrenic" symptomatology responded to removal from home with a modification of his clinical picture. This suggests that symptoms classed "first rank" by Schneider are more deeply embedded, or to use Astrup's (1962) term, are "mental automatisms" as opposed to psychodynamically understandable (and modifiable?) phenomena.

Body-build and heredity of late schizophrenics are generally agreed to deviate less from the normal than in early onset cases. Schizophrenia in late life has been found more rarely associated with leptosomatic or dysplastic types of body-build (Kolle, 1931; Hirschmann and Klages, 1957; Sjoegren, 1964), though Kay and Roth (1961) denied a predominance of pyknic features in their late paraphrenics. Confirming the observations of the earlier workers, exact anthropometric measurements obtained from a sample of our paranoid subjects did not differ in any respect from those of elderly depressives (Lodge-Patch, Post and Slater, 1965), and the differences found on these measures between younger schizophrenics and manic-depressives did not occur in illnesses of late onset.

There is a similar consensus concerning the reduced importance of hereditary factors, not only in late depressions (Post, 1962) but also in schizophrenic breakdowns of late life. Funding (1961) reported on patients who developed paranoid delusions not clearly derived from the prevailing mood after the age of 50. Their discharge diagnoses had, however, been of a schizophrenic type in not quite one-half, the rest being classified as manic-depressive, psychogenic, or atypical. Among first-degree relatives of all 148 probands, he ascertained 21 schizophrenics, 15 manic-depressives, and 18 with the Scandinavian (Faergeman, 1963) diagnosis of "psychogenic psychosis". Funding calculated that the expectancy of schizophrenia in siblings was 2·5 per cent, significantly greater than in the general population (0·9 per cent), but also significantly lower than that for siblings of younger schizophrenics (7·4 per cent). Klages (1961) found among 53 schizophrenics starting their illnesses between 40 and 60 (and none of them over 60 at the time of admission), only 8 schizophrenic first-degree relatives, and 7 depressives. Like other workers, he stated that the tendency for late-onset schizophrenias to occur more frequently in the families of late schizophrenics did not exceed the general finding of a tendency for relatives to become psychotic around the same age as probands. Kay (1963) reported among some 50 late paraphrenics in a Stockholm Hospital, 13 secondary cases of schizophrenia among parents (2), siblings (8), and children (3). He also calculated a morbidity risk among siblings which was considerably below that given for those of younger schizophrenics. In his material, he discovered only 5 or 6 relatives with affective disorders, most of them in one way or other atypical.

Our enquiry was not specifically directed towards hereditary-genetic matters, but an admission of psychiatric disorders in relatives was obtained in 43 of 93 patients. Under these circumstances, our discovering only 5 schizophrenic first-degree relatives was not out of keeping with previous work. None of them were, however, very typical, to judge from the descriptions obtainable (only one was personally examined, as she was admitted with her sister, but excluded on account of an early onset). Two were also "late schizophrenics". More surprising was the fact that 16 first-degree relatives were supposed to have suffered from affective disorders, most of which were associated with hospital admissions and/or suicidal attempts. To complete the picture, 27 had milder personality disorders including alcoholism, and 8 had suffered from organic mental disorders including epilepsy. It might be suggested that (with the exception of Funding) earlier workers had been stricter in their diagnostic criteria of late schizophrenia or paraphrenia (though this is not suggested by perusal of their case records). As a matter of fact, probands with the diagnostically least controversial "schizophrenic" syndrome did have a relatively larger number of schizophrenic and a smaller number of affective relatives than the "schizophreniform" or paranoid hallucinosis patients, but the small numbers and the doubtful quality of our data (many failures to obtain a positive family history were due to unavailability or unreliability of the informants) precludes the use of significance tests (Table 5).

TABLE 5. INCIDENCE AND TYPE OF POSITIVE FAMILY HISTORY RELATED TO CLINICAL SYNDROME OF PROBANDS

Psychiatric disorders in other members of family	Clinical syndrome of proband			Total
	Paranoid hallucinosis	Schizo-phreniform syndrome	Schizo-phrenic syndrome	
Denied	10	20	20	50
Admitted	12	17	14	43
	22	37	34	93

Diagnostic category of affected relative	Number of affected first-degree relatives per syndrome of proband			Total
	Paranoid hallucinosis	Schizo-phreniform syndrome	Schizo-phrenic syndrome	
? Schizophrenia	1	1	3	5
? Affective psychosis	4	8	4	16
Neurosis and personality disorders	7	14	6	27
Organic psychosyndrome	1	2	5	8
	13	25	18	56

In summary, elderly paranoid patients tended to fall into one of three relatively homogenous syndromes: in paranoid hallucinosis, auditory hallucinations were the only type of psychotic experience associated with false beliefs of persecution; in the "schizophreniform" syndrome, there were multiple sources of abnormal experiences, but at a pinch, and allowing for the patient's cultural background, social or sensory deprivation, they remained understandable. Patients with the "schizophrenic" syndrome had, in addition, Schneider's symptoms of first-rank, such as a special type of auditory hallucinosis, and or experiences which could be conceptualised only by assuming deep-going disruptions of the patient's personality and world. The more profound, elemental, or archetypal character of these "first-rank", "process" or "schizophrenic" symptoms was supported by the finding that they (in contrast with other paranoid symptoms) never disappeared when the patient was brought into a less stressful environment. In other respects, however, "schizophrenic" syndrome patients differed from those with a "schizophreniform" symptomatology or with a paranoid hallucinosis only very slightly in a way that might suggest that they were purer or more complete derivatives of a nuclear schizophrenic prototype. Patients classified in our special sense as "schizophrenic" were much more often judged to exhibit a subtle defect of the way in which they were able to communicate their feeling tone and to put themselves over by expression and gesture. At the same time, there were in their mental state slightly fewer depressive admixtures, and a smaller preponderance of affective as against schizophrenic illnesses among first-degree relatives. On the other hand, the presence of pathological brain changes was not specifically associated with any one paranoid syndrome, nor were social or sensory deprivation any commoner in the more "understandable" psychoses.

CHAPTER 5

Methods of Treatment and its Effects

It will be recalled that the present investigation was intended to test an impression that the outlook for paranoid illnesses of old age had been signally improved by the introduction of phenothiazine drugs. At the same time, it was hoped that this study might shed some light on more basic and theoretical issues, possibly by comparing the impact of treatment on different symptom clusters within the schizophrenic reaction type, as manifested in late life. Before addressing ourselves to these matters, we shall describe methods and effects of treatment in a more general way.

As was set out earlier (Table 1), 20 of the patients admitted during phase I of this study did not at any time receive adequate amounts of phenothiazine therapy. During phase II, 37 patients admitted up to February 1961 received full courses of these drugs as in-patients, while during the subsequent phase III, some members of a further sample of 32 patients received this therapy as out-patients. From having been experimental during phase II, experiences in phase III had consolidated the drug treatment of elderly paranoid patients to a considerable extent. Out-patient treatment is now preferred, provided there are no suicidal tendencies, and the patients' complaints and behaviour disorders can be tolerated by their friends for a little longer. Patients living alone or in poor social contact should be admitted, as unsupervised patients tend to fail their appointments right from the beginning (2 in this series) or are more unreliable in taking their tablets than are patients living with members of their families. By the very fact of coming for a consultation, patients appear to betray a modicum of "insight", but it has not been found helpful to try and make them aware of this. The main line of approach is to build up a trusting relationship, which is best promoted by accepting the patient's accounts without criticism, and by expressing regret at their having to pass through such a difficult time: their nerves have been affected by all these experiences, and the tablets which are about to be prescribed will place them in a better position of resisting these onslaughts against their health. Patients approached in this way, and given a sympathetic and uncritical hearing (so very different from the attitude of their much-tried friends) are more likely to accept the psychiatrist and his treatment.

Type of drug. During phase II, treatment with trifluoperazine alone was given to 32 patients; 4 had chlorpromazine as the only preparation, and 5 had either both or also one or two other preparations in succession. Changes of drug were due to jaundice or diarrhoea during chlorpromazine treatment in two cases, and due to failure to respond in the remainder. Dosages of all preparations were gradually increased until symptoms disappeared and anti-parkinsonian preparations were given as required. Most patients responded by the time a daily intake of 15–25 mg of trifluoperazine had been reached, usually during the third or fourth week of treatment. No relationship was found to exist between size of dosage, or rate of its increase, and any clinical features.

Further experiences during the third phase of the investigation may be given in some detail. Up to the early summer of 1963, trifluoperazine had remained the preparation of first choice. The frequency with which various dosages were reached during the early weeks of treatment is given in Table 6. Again, most patients required 15 mg daily, a dose reached after 2–3 weeks, before symptoms cleared. Twelve of eighteen patients developed side-effects, mostly necessitating the exhibition of anti-parkinsonian preparations. It will be noted that one patient, though on the biggest daily dose, did not show any drug reactions (though he gradually lost his symptoms). Almost certainly, he avoided taking some of his tablets by various stratagems, which are well known to be successful even in units with high nurse–patient ratios. All but 5 patients were sooner or later taken off trifluoperazine for one or the other of the following reasons: failure to respond either initially or on relapse (4); slowness anergia, depressive moods or restlessness (6); one patient developing an organic confusional state which was almost certainly

TABLE 6. MAXIMUM DOSAGES REACHED. NUMBERS OF PATIENTS SHOWING TROUBLESOME SIDE-EFFECTS OF EITHER DRUG IN BRACKETS. (Third series only.)

Daily amounts of trifluoperazine (mg)	Number of patients	Daily amounts of thioridazine (mg)	Number of patients
60	1 (0)	600	2 (2)
35	1 (1)	300	2 (1)
24	1 (1)	250	1 (0)
20	3 (2)	225	2 (0)
15	9 (7)	200	2 (0)
10	3 (1)	150	2 (1)
		100	1 (0)
		75	2 (lapsed at once)
	18 (12)		14 (4)

due to excessive amounts of an anti-parkinsonian preparation. The most serious toxic effect observed in this last sample of patients was severe anaemia with granulopenia in one. This also occurred when the trifluoperazine was replaced by thioridazine and the patient finally had to be transferred to another hospital for long-term care. Two members of the earlier series developed the syndrome of abnormal movements which since then has been described by Hunter, Earl and Thornicroft (1964; see also an editorial in the *Brit. Med. J.* **2,** 1412 (1964). One patient (in the first series) had a "schizophrenic" psychosis which failed to respond even after she had received 45–80 mg of trifluoperazine over many months. Eighteen months after this was discontinued on account of a severe hypermotility syndrome she still exhibited slight abnormal movements though in contrast to Hunter's patients the severe writhings, mouthings, and tongue protrusions had ceased. Reversibility of this syndrome has been reported since (Kilpatrick and Whyte, 1965). (Incidently, this patient's psychotic symptoms disappeared with the onset of abnormal movements, and when later they returned proved far less disturbing.) Similar but less severe phenomena were observed in an equally intractable patient after his dosage had reached 90 mg. Experience suggests that there is little point in raising trifluoperazine beyond 30 mg a day in elderly patients.

On account of the frequency of more minor neurological side-effects, but more importantly of anergic-depressive changes, trifluoperazine was displaced by thioridazine as the preparation of first choice from about May 1963 onwards. According to Remy (1962), neither visual impairment nor retinal changes were discovered in more than 100 patients treated for up to 5 years within a daily dosage range of 150–600 mg, and this was never exceeded in the course of this study. Fourteen patients in the present series were treated from the start with thioridazine (Table 6). Eleven patients were treated with this preparation alone (but two defaulted while only receiving 75 mg). One patient received (erroneously) promazine as well. One patient did a little better when changed to trifluoperazine, but another one did badly on chlorpromazine, and later on lost all her symptoms when again placed on thioridazine (this patient had originally resisted taking her tablets!). Table 6 also demonstrates that far fewer patients on thioridazine exhibited side-effects; anti-parkinson drugs were given in only 2 instances. Anergic or agitated depressive mood changes were far less often encountered in relation to thioridazine therapy. Including our first series, 50 patients were initially treated with trifluoperazine, and *at later date* 10 were given anti-depressive therapies (imipramine, 7; ECT, 2; and one patient had both forms of treatment). By contrast, only one of the 14 patients treated with thioridazine from the start was

TABLE 7. TYPE OF DRUG AND MAINTENANCE DOSAGES IN 18 PATIENTS BELONGING TO THE THIRD SAMPLE AND SUCCESSFULLY CONTINUING ON MAINTENANCE THERAPY

Thioridazine (daily mg)	Number of patients	Trifluo-perazine (daily mg)	Number of patients	Other pheno-thiazines	Number of patients
400	1	10	1		1
300	2	5	3		
150	3				
100	2				
75	3				
50	2				
	13		4		1

later on given imipramine as well; this occurred at another hospital, to which she had been admitted on relapse. Information on dosages and preparations used in maintenance therapy of the last sample of patients is set out in Table 7.

Early results of treatment. None of the 24 patients admitted during the first phase of this investigation lost his paranoid symptoms. It will be recalled that this first series of subjects did not receive any phenothiazine drugs in adequate amounts during their index admission, and apart from 4 patients receiving these drugs at a later date, they continued to exhibit symptoms throughout the follow-up period of 3 years (see next section). One instance of "spontaneous" recovery appears to have occurred, however, in a patient belonging to the third sample. The evidence for this is rather dubious, and for this reason, the facts are herewith submitted:

A widow, *aet.* 63, had changed flats three times in the preceding 4 or 5 years, because she felt people were annoying her to get her out, were making noises, and were using an electrical vibrator machine which caused her to lose weight. These experiences were limited to her home, where she lived alone in little contact with her family. She was placed on 75 mg of thioridazine, and the PSW visited and arranged her attendance at an old peoples' club. She was not, however, able to persuade the patient to return to the clinic, and she probably never took any of the prescribed tablets. Surprisingly, the patient finally kept a follow-up appointment 16 months later, after several failures (explained by letters in red ink). She confirmed that she had had no further treatment, denied any symptoms, and intimated that her previous experiences must have been imaginary. As before, she refused access to her relatives, but it was noteworthy that she was still at the same address, and she claimed to have refused rehousing, as the offered flat would have been too long a distance away from her club.

The immediate results of treatment in patients who received adequate amounts of phenothiazine drugs as soon as a diagnosis of a non-depressive paranoid illness had been made are set out in Table 8.

Complete or almost complete failure to modify pathological experiences and thought content occurred in only 6 patients of the 71 receiving adequate initial courses of drug treatment. Twenty-two continued to have abnormal experiences or to entertain delusional beliefs, but the intensity of their symptoms was markedly diminished, and it seemed likely that the patients would be able to live with their disorders without causing any frequent or unmanageable difficulties. It was thought that 43 patients made

TABLE 8. IMMEDIATE RESULTS OF DRUG THERAPY IN PATIENTS RECEIVING PHENOTHIAZINES IN ADEQUATE AMOUNTS FROM THE BEGINNING OF TREATMENT

Number of patients	Short-term results of phenothiazine treatment				Total
	Defaulted immediately	No change	Partial remission	Complete remission	
In 2nd series (incl. 4 members of 1st series)	—	4	12	25	41
In 3rd series	2	2	10	18	32
	2	6	22	43	73

complete responses to drug therapy, in that they ceased to have any psychotic experiences or to harbour any current persecutory ideas. The proportions of patients making these three kinds of immediate response to treatment were very similar in the two consecutive samples.

Insight, like many other psychiatric terms, is a concept which loses any true meaning when one tries to define and critically analyse it. Operationally, one might say that patients in this series who stated that their past experiences had been imaginary, and must have been due to being "like in a dream" or to having been "mentally deranged", had achieved "full insight". Statements of this type were made by only 14 of the 71 patients who had received full courses of drug therapy. This degree of insight was maintained throughout the observation period by only 8 patients; 4 lost their insight, and 2 gained it only at a later date. Nine patients showed "partial insight" at some time or other (6 throughout), in that they half-realised that their experiences might have been imaginary ("If you say so, doctor"—or conflicting statements about "insight" in the same or in subsequent interviews). The overwhelming majority of patients never gained any insight whatsoever, even when they had completely lost all their symptoms (see Table 9). Either they professed bewilderment, or more often they would say that the persecutions had stopped for various reasons. They would, however, remain firmly convinced of the reality of their past experiences.

TABLE 9. RESPONSE TO PHENOTHIAZINE TREATMENT RELATED TO DEGREE OF "INSIGHT" ACHIEVED.
(Patients in all three samples who had full courses of drugs at some time.)

Degree of "insight"	Response to phenothiazine therapy			Total
	None	Partial	Complete	
None	6	19	23	48
Partial	—	1	8	9
Complete	—	2	12	14
	6	22	43	71

We shall see that the achievement of a modicum of "insight" turned out to be a favourable prognostic feature, but also that many patients continued with drug maintenance treatment and remained well, though continuing to deny that they had ever "imagined it all". Perhaps such behaviour is an aspect of schizophrenic ambivalence!

Long-term outcome could be assessed fully in the first two series of patients who had all been followed over 3 years (unless, of course, they had died at an earlier date); in the third series, the follow-through had varied between 6 and 41 months (Table 10) and the period at risk for changes to occur varied considerably.

TABLE 10. METHOD AND LENGTH OF FOLLOW-UP OF THIRD SERIES

Length of follow-up period (in months)	Personal throughout	Initially personal; final information from other sources	Reports only	Total
Under 6	3	—	—	3
7—12	2	1	—	3
13—18	9	2	1	12
19—24	4	—	—	4
25—36	4	2	1	7
37 and over	—	3	—	3
	22	8	2	32

In assessing long-term results, it will therefore be necessary to treat the first two samples separately from the third, but in all three samples we shall omit patients who died during the first year under observation, incidentally removing from this area of enquiry all those paranoid patients whose brain damage was sufficiently severe to seriously shorten their immediate expectation of life. In the first two samples, we are then left with 56 patients, and after omitting not only one patient dying but also 3 irretrievably lost from the follow-up during the first year, there are 28 subjects in the third sample.

In terms of drug therapy, 19 of the 56 patients in the first two series never received any adequate doses of phenothiazines ("no treatment"); 16 did receive adequate courses, but failure of maintenance therapy occurred ("partial treatment"); finally, 21 patients not only had full courses of drugs but, in addition, maintenance therapy was fully achieved ("full treatment"). One way of describing long-term outcome of any severe and disabling illness and of relating it to type and intensity of treatment is to use the amount of time spent in hospital as one's yardstick. For several patients, the 3-year observation period was cut short by deaths during the second and third year, and length of hospital stay is not therefore given (in Table 11) as months, but as the proportion of follow-up period "alive".

TABLE 11. RELATIONSHIP BETWEEN TREATMENT AND DURATION OF IN-PATIENT CARE

Proportion of follow-up during which patients were in psychiatric hospitals (in %)	"No treatment"	"Partial treatment"	"Full treatment"	Total
3—8	8	3	6	17
11—15	2	4	6	12
17—25	2	5	7	14
31—97	4	3	2	9
100	3	1	—	4
	19	16	21	56

It will be seen that the overwhelming majority of patients spent only relatively short periods (which included their index admissions) in hospital, and that only 4 patients could never be discharged at all. Moreover, there was no very striking gradient of the durations of stay comparing "fully", "partially" or "not treated" patients in the expected direction of shorter hospital stays in relation to more efficient drug therapy. This tendency for our elderly paranoid patients to be discharged from hospital and to remain, regardless of the kind and intensity of treatment given, in the community, sets them apart from those in public mental hospitals (Fish, 1960). Almost certainly this difference is due to a selection bias, in that elderly patients are admitted to area mental hospitals much more often as a last resort and because they cannot be supported in the community any longer, while a teaching hospital tends to admit more patients who themselves have a desire for help, or with relatives and friends anxious to obtain some curative treatment rather than long-term care for them. Our sample of patients was characterised by a high proportion with reasonably good interpersonal relationships, which permitted them to live outside institutions, in spite of the continued presence of mental symptoms.

However, Table 12 records that all 19 patients who never received any adequate phenothiazine drugs remained ill throughout the entire observation period. Such complete failure for any

TABLE 12. RELATIONSHIP BETWEEN MEMBERSHIP OF TREATMENT GROUP AND LONG-TERM COURSE OF ILLNESS

Proportion of follow-up during which symptoms were present (in %)	"No treatment"	"Partial treatment"	"Full treatment"	Total
3–11	—	—	12	12
22–35	—	2	2	4
50–67	—	2	2	4
75–95	—	4	2	6
100	19	8	3	30
	19	16	21	56

remission to occur was seen in 8 of the 16 patients who had adequate drug therapy for a time, and in only 3 of 21 receiving full maintenance therapy throughout. Only in patients receiving full maintenance therapy did we achieve a considerable shortening of the period of mental ill-health, to less than 4 months in the case of 12 patients. Earlier, we reported that some patients lost their "active" (for definition see p. 31) psychotic symptoms on removal from their home surroundings. This encapsulation of active symptoms also occurred without environmental changes during the course of the follow-through, but much more rarely in the

TABLE 13. RELATIONSHIP BETWEEN TREATMENT AND TIME DURING WHICH PATIENTS REMAINED "ACTIVELY PSYCHOTIC"

Proportion of follow-up during which patients were "actively psychotic" (in %)	"No treatment"	"Partial treatment"	"Full treatment"	Total
0–3	1	1	3	5
6–11	1	1	10	12
17–35	2	2	5	9
53–66	—	5	—	5
75–97	2	6	2	10
100	13	1	1	15
	19	16	21	56

completely untreated than in the partially and fully treated groups (Table 13). The proportions of follow-up period (FUP) during which patients had no mental symptoms whatever, were actively experiencing abnormal phenomena, or were merely deluded in retrospect and apprehensive, were combined to yield five types of outcome:

Either type of mental symptoms during	3–11% of FUP	Class 1
	22–35% of FUP	Class 2
	50–95% of FUP	Class 3
Mental symptoms, but not "actively psychotic" for	100% of FUP	Class 4
"Actively psychotic" during	100% of FUP	Class 5

In our sample of 56 patients surviving the first year of a 3-year observation period, outcome was clearly related to the use of phenothiazine therapy (Table 14). All 19 patients who never received this form of treatment in an adequate fashion remained continously mentally ill, though 6 lost their "active" symptoms which, as in all patients of these samples, had been responsible for their admission. By contrast, all the 12 patients who recovered

TABLE 14. RELATIONSHIP BETWEEN TREATMENT AND LONG-TERM OUTCOME

Outcome class	"No treatment"	"Partial treatment"	"Full treatment"	Total
Class 1	—	—	12	12
Class 2	—	2	2	4
Class 3	—	6	4	10
Class 4	6	7	2	15
Class 5	13	1	1	15
	19	16	21	56

completely and quickly, and remained well, had received full and maintained drug treatment, conditions under which only 3 of 21 patients failed to lose all symptoms at some time or other. When maintenance drug therapy was not achieved, moderately successful results only were obtained, and that in only half the patients. Comparing Classes 1–3 with Classes 4–5, the relationship between intensity of treatment and long-term clinical outcome became a highly significant one ($X^2=29{\cdot}5741$; d.f.$=2$; $p<{\cdot}001$).

Turning to the third research sample of 28 patients, followed for periods varying between one and a little over 3 years, any classification of long-term outcome, and any comparison with the results achieved in the earlier samples (who were all followed for the same period of 3 years) can only be provisional and tentative. So far, 10 patients have been entirely symptom-free for almost the whole time during which they have been followed. This favourable outcome, which is equivalent to that of fully followed patients in Class 1, will be called outcome A. Eleven patients either responded fully to treatment only rather late, or exhibited mild and occasional symptoms throughout; the progress of these patients provisionally placed in Class B was roughly equivalent to that of Class 2 and Class 3 patients. Finally, like members of Classes 4 and 5, there were 7 patients (Class C) who remained continuously disabled by psychotic symptoms, though only 4 have so far required frequent or long-term hospital care. It will be seen (Table 15) that the proportions of patients in whom maintenance of adequate drug therapy failed are very similar in both research samples. Taking the results of both samples together (a not entirely correct procedure in view of the shorter average follow-up of the last series) it can be

TABLE 15. LONG-TERM OUTCOME RELATED TO SUCCESS IN MAINTAINING DRUG THERAPY

2nd Sample
Maintenance Therapy

Outcome	Achieved	Failed	Total
1	12	—	12
2 + 3	6	8	14
4 + 5	3	8	11
	21	16	37

3rd Sample
Maintenance therapy

Outcome	Achieved	Failed	Total
A	9	1	10
B	7	4	11
C	2	5	7
	18	10	28

Both series
Maintenance therapy

Outcome	Achieved	Failed	Total
1 + A	21	1	22
2 + 3 + B	13	12	25
4 + 5 + C	5	13	18
	39	26	65

shown that there is a significant relationship between success in maintaining treatment and quality of long-term results ($X^2 = 19 \cdot 9764$; d.f.=2; $p < \cdot 001$).

Social outcome. Removal of symptoms is only one aim of psychiatric treatment, which is of little value if it does not also improve, or prevent deterioration of, more general personality functioning, especially in the areas of life performance and personal relationships. In assessing the more general progress of elderly paranoid patients, we shall omit all those who had suffered from confirmed brain changes or were lost from the follow-up during the first year, in order to eliminate most physical factors which might have interfered with general adjustment. In the remaining 71 patients, most of whom were followed over 3 years, there was some decline of occupational adjustment in only 19. Originally, 52 patients had either been gainfully employed or effectively engaged in household tasks; at follow-up, this number had fallen to 35, and 18 (compared with 2 initially) were practically unoccupied (Table 16). Against

TABLE 16. CHANGES IN ACTIVITIES DURING OBSERVATION PERIOD
(Patients dying or lost during the first year and suffering from confirmed cerebral disorders have been omitted.)

At follow-up	Around time of onset				Total
	Gainfully employed	Domestic duties, efficiently	Domestic duties, largely ineffectually	Practically unoccupied	
Gainfully employed	5	1	—	—	6
Domestic duties, efficiently	3	26	—	—	29
Domestic duties ineffectually	2	7	9	—	18
Practically unoccupied	—	8	8	2	18
	10	42	17	2	71

expectation, poor clinical outcome was only weakly related to low occupational status at follow-up (Table 17). It will be noticed that 2 patients were in gainful employment while remaining psychotic and, at the other extreme, that 4 patients had remained symptom-free but were completely unoccupied. Most patients did not show any movement up or down a four-step scale, descending from "gainfully employed", "domestic duties efficiently", and "domestic duties inefficiently" to "practically unoccupied". Only one patient

TABLE 17. STATUS IN TERMS OF ACTIVITIES AT FOLLOW-UP RELATED TO CLINICAL OUTCOME

Clinical outcome	At follow-up				Total
	Gainfully employed	Domestic duties, effectively	Domestic duties, inefficiently	Practically unoccupied	
A + 1	3	11	2	4	20
B + 2 + 3	1	9	6	4	20
C + 4 + 5	2	9	10	10	31
	6	29	18	18	71

increased her activities by taking up part-time work, but 28 declined in occupational level. Again, this decline was not related to clinical outcome (Table 18), or to the intensity of drug therapy

TABLE 18. CHANGES IN THE AREA OF ACTIVITIES RELATED TO CLINICAL OUTCOME

Clinical outcome	Changes of activity +1	0	−1	−2	Total
A + 1	1	12	5	2	20
B + 2 + 3	—	11	7	2	20
C + 4 + 5	—	19	6	6	31
	1	42	18	10	71

TABLE 19. CHANGES IN ACTIVITIES RELATED TO THE INTENSITY OF DRUG TREATMENT

Drug therapy	Changes of activity +1	0	−1	−2	Total
None or inadequate	—	11	4	2	17
Adequate at some time	—	13	5	3	21
Adequate, maintained	1	18	9	5	33
	1	42	18	10	71

(Table 19). In the area of social relationships, closeness and harmony of interactions did not alter noticeably in 48 of 71 persons. In a few it increased, and in a somewhat larger proportion it declined. There was a slight association between clinical outcome and changes in social integration in the expected parallel direction (Table 20),

TABLE 20. CHANGES IN SOCIAL RELATIONSHIPS RELATED TO CLINICAL OUTCOME

Clinical outcome	Changes in social integration			Total
	Improvement	No change	Decline	
A + 1	5	12	3	20
B + 2 + 3	1	13	6	20
C + 4 + 5	1	23	7	31
	7	48	16	71

but these changes were not related to the intensity of drug treatment. Finally, by combining changes in the occupational area with those in relationships, rough estimates of changes in the patients' life-adjustment were obtained. Again, almost one-half experienced no alterations in general adjustment, only 5 improved, 16 declined slightly, and 17 more severely. Clinical outcome related only very slightly positively or negatively to general adjustment (Table 21), which correlate even less with intensity of drug therapy (Table 22).

TABLE 21. CHANGES IN GENERAL ADJUSTMENT RELATED TO CLINICAL OUTCOME

Clinical outcome	Changes in general adjustment					Total
	Moderate improvement	Slight improvement	No change	Slight decline	Moderate decline	
A + 1	1	3	7	6	3	20
B + 2 + 3	—	—	10	5	5	20
C + 4 + 5	—	1	16	5	9	31
	1	4	33	16	17	71

TABLE 22. CHANGES IN GENERAL ADJUSTMENT RELATED TO INTENSITY OF DRUG TREATMENT

Drug therapy	Changes in general adjustment					Total
	Moderate improvement	Slight improvement	No change	Slight decline	Moderate decline	
None or inadequate	—	—	11	2	4	17
Adequate, at some time	—	1	10	4	6	21
Adequate, maintained	1	3	12	10	7	33
	1	4	33	16	17	71

None of these data has been submitted to tests of statistical significance, and this not only on account of varying observation periods; in addition, and in contradistinction of our findings in elderly depressives, the onset of illnesses had been ill-defined in most cases, and it was therefore often difficult to make a reliable assessment of the patient's original adjustment. Furthermore, a detailed follow-up of these paranoid people proved much more difficult than the earlier one of depressives, and the assessment of social changes often amounted to no more than an estimate made on rather scanty evidence. It was not, therefore, admissible to combine social and symptom changes into different types of global outcome, as had been done in the previous study of patients with affective symptoms. All one can state is that over a period of 2 or 3 years, 33 of 71 patients (46·5 per cent) declined in their general life-adjustment, that 33 (46·5 per cent) remained stable, and that only 5 (7 per cent) improved (Table 21). These figures may be contrasted with those obtained in 70 elderly depressives, observed over 6 years (extracted from Table 18, p. 56, 1962): social decline was registered in a very similar proportion, 44·3 per cent; no social change had occurred in 31·4 per cent, while 24·3 per cent had improved in their general adjustment. Social status was, moreover, highly significantly related to clinical course in affective patients, there being a strong impression that social changes, if any, were secondary to clinical phenomena. The course of paranoid illnesses was, as we saw (Table 21), hardly related to social changes; those few patients who improved their adjustment almost all had good clinical outcomes, but a number of those doing well symptomatically deteriorated socially. However, poor clinical results were hardly any more often associated with social deterioration. Possibly, these paradoxical results are due to the research sample of paranoid patients having been drawn from favourable social backgrounds, which cushioned any unfavourable further progress. On the other hand, the patient's personalities, which as we shall see had in many instances been deviant for many years, might have created a human environment which was little influenced in its tolerance and acceptance by further worsening or improvement of a psychosis, when this eventually supervened.

In summary, a regime has been described which in a large proportion of elderly paranoid patients led to cessation or marked improvement of mental disturbance. Success or failure were highly significantly related to the adequacy of therapy with phenothiazine drugs and its long-term maintenance. Most patients in this sample came from a tolerant social background, and their social adjustment was only to a slight extent altered by the course taken by their illness. Removal of symptoms only very rarely led to improvement of social circumstances in these elderly paranoid patients in contrast with the results obtained in depressives. Next, we shall examine whether it is possible to discover prognostic factors which are not, or less obviously, related to the success of drug therapy.

CHAPTER 6

Prognostic Factors

Before looking for features related to long-term outcome in the symptomatology, personality and social background of our sample of paranoid patients, two prognostic factors will be discussed which refer to the initial effects of phenothiazine treatment.

The immediate response to adequate drug therapy was found to be a potentially useful indicator of the ultimate outcome. This was clearly demonstrated in the second research sample, whose members had been fully treated initially, and who were all followed up for

TABLE 23. THE IMMEDIATE RESPONSE TO PHENOTHIAZINE DRUGS RELATED TO LONG-TERM OUTCOME

2nd Sample

Outcome	Immediate response		Total
	Complete	Incomplete	
1	11	1	12
2 + 3	10	4	14
4 + 5	1	10	11
	22	15	37

3rd Sample

Outcome	Immediate response		Total
	Complete	Incomplete	
A	7	3	10
B	6	5	11
C	3	4	7
	16	12	28

Both samples

Outcome	Immediate response		Total
	Complete	Incomplete	
A + 1	18	4	22
B + 2 + 3	16	9	25
C + 4 + 5	4	14	18
	38	27	65

3 years (1st table in Table 23). The tendency for complete initial remission of symptoms to be associated with a more favourable long-term course, and incomplete remission with an unfavourable one, was very much in excess of chance expectation ($X^2=17 \cdot 5631$; d.f.$=2$; $p< \cdot 001$). This trend was rather less impressive in the last sample, possibly because some patients were treated less effectively initially when they attended only as out-patients, or because in most patients the follow-up period was less than 3 years. (All the same, both samples together still yielded $X^2=14 \cdot 9828$; d.f.$=2$; $p< \cdot 001$.)

Gaining a modicum of "insight" turned out to be another favourable prognostic sign, whose value was slightly diminished by the fact that a few patients gained some insight only late in the course of treatment, and that in others it was variable (see p. 40). Table 24 records the extent to which full or at least some realisation of the pathological nature of his beliefs and experiences was associated with

TABLE 24. THE PROGNOSTIC SIGNIFICANCE OF GAINING INSIGHT

Outcome	"Insight" Full or some	"Insight" None	Total
A + 1	14	8	22
B + 2 + 3	8	17	25
C + 4 + 5	—	18	18
	22	43	65

a favourable course of the patient's illness (proportions similar for both treated samples; for combined sample, $X^2=17 \cdot 9491$; d.f.$=2$; $p< \cdot 001$).

Success in maintaining long-term drug therapy was earlier (Table 15 and p. 46) shown to have been highly significantly associated with a favourable outcome. Failure of maintenance treatment was due to three causes: (1) lack of co-operation by family doctors, which occurred only once or twice; (2) idiosyncrasy to all drugs given a trial, a contingency met with equally rarely; and (3) failure on the part of patients to co-operate in maintenance therapy for reasons which will be investigated presently. Omitting patients in whose cases long-term treatment failed for reasons obviously outside their control, it was shown that in both samples favourable immediate

TABLE 25. RELATIONSHIP BETWEEN IMMEDIATE RESPONSE TO TREATMENT AND SUCCESS OR FAILURE OF MAINTENANCE THERAPY IN ALL PATIENTS SURVIVING THE FIRST YEAR OF THE FOLLOW-UP

2nd sample

Immediate response to treatment	Co-operation maintained	Further co-operation failed	Total
Complete	17	5	22
Partial or none	7	8	15
	24	13	37

3rd sample

Immediate response to treatment	Co-operation maintained	Further co-operation failed	Total
Complete	12	4	16
Partial or none	6	6	12
	18	10	28

Both series combined

Immediate response to treatment	Co-operation maintained	Further co-operation failed	Total
Complete	29	9	38
Partial or none	13	14	27
	42	23	65

TABLE 26. CO-OPERATION IN MAINTENANCE THERAPY RELATED TO REALISATION OF ILLNESS

2nd sample

"Insight"	Co-operation maintained	Further co-operation failed	Total
Full or some	11	1	12
None	13	12	25
	24	13	37

3rd sample

"Insight"	Co-operation maintained	Further co-operation failed	Total
Full or some	8	2	10
None	10	8	18
	18	10	28

Both series combined

"Insight"	Co-operation maintained	Further co-operation failed	Total
Full or some	19	3	22
None	23	20	43
	42	23	65

response to treatment was related to full further co-operation by the patient (Table 25, for both samples together, $X^2=4\cdot3148$; d.f.$=1$; $p<\cdot05$). Similarly, fully maintained co-operation was also positively associated with achievement of at least some "insight" (Table 26, for both samples together, $X^2=5\cdot5169$; d.f.$=1$; $p<\cdot02$).

E

Good immediate therapeutic response and the gaining of some degree of insight could therefore be seen to be favourable factors, largely because they were linked with continued co-operativeness on the part of the patient. We shall presently encounter several other variables more frequently seen in patients doing relatively well, again because on closer analysis they are characteristics of patients who continue to co-operate with treatment. There will be increasing evidence that these direct and indirect associations are likely to be of a causal significance.

Unfavourable prognostic factors in untreated patients. Only 4 patients of the first research sample (1954–9) received adequate amounts of phenothiazine preparations at a later stage, and none of the others recovered. Of the 19 surviving the first year of the follow-up period, 6 settled down into states where their symptoms were no longer "active" (as defined on p. 31). These numbers and trifling differences in outcome were too small to permit of the isolation of prognostic factors within this group of untreated elderly paranoid patients, and there does not seem to have been any previous study of factors promoting "social recoveries" from this hitherto therapeutically unrewarding condition. We saw (Table 14 and p. 45) that elderly paraphrenics followed over the same period, but treated at least for a time with adequate amounts of phenothiazines, had a significantly better outcome than untreated patients. The question obviously arises, whether factors other than drug therapy could have been responsible for the striking discrepancy in long-term results of our first and second samples.

One difference stands out: after their initial period in hospital, patients in the first sample (being at that time regarded as incurable) were only rarely seen again by the investigator or his co-workers (Table 1); by contrast, considerable efforts were made to keep in personal contact with the patients in both the other samples throughout the follow-up period. We shall return to the role of the doctor–patient relationship in a later section.

Table 27 records that patients in the second (and drug-treated) sample tended to have been ill for shorter periods and to have been a little more often below the age of 70 ($X^2=3\cdot9956$; d.f.$=1$; $p < \cdot05$). However, the associated "excess" of widows in the untreated sample was not beyond chance expectation, nor were deafness or the

Table 27. Comparing the Frequencies of Certain Variables of Untreated and Treated Patients in the First Two Research Samples

Social and clinical variables	Phenothiazine therapy		Total
	None or inadequate	Adequate at some time	
Number of patients	20	41	61
Age			
Below 70	6	25	31
70 and over	14	16	30
Civil status			
Widowed	13	14	27
Married	4	14	18
Single	3	9	12
Separated and divorced	—	4	4
Socio-occupational status			
Professional and independent	1	5	6
Skilled	5	12	17
Semi-skilled and unskilled	14	24	38
Personal relationships			
Sharing home, mainly harmoniously	7	16	23
Sharing home, poor relationships	3	7	10
Living alone, with good relations	4	9	13
Living alone, largely unfriendly	4	8	12
Completely isolated, or institutionalised	2	1	3
Cerebral pathology			
Confirmed	2	12	14
Suspected	3	8	11
Absent	15	21	36
Hearing			
Impaired	9	10	19
Clinical syndrome			
Paranoid hallucinosis	4	8	12
"Schizophreniform" syndrome	7	18	25
"Schizophrenic" syndrome	9	15	24
Duration of illness			
Less than 1 year	8	21	29
1–3 years	7	9	16
4 years and over	5	11	16

preponderance of socially low-class persons. The second sample contained a larger proportion of cerebral-organic cases, no doubt the result of an effort, at the time, of bringing into hospital all elderly paranoid patients to study the effects of modern drug-therapy, even when the general prognosis seemed prima facie bad. In spite of their greater age, more frequent occurrence of the widowed state, and of deafness, the untreated sample did not have a greater proportion of persons with poor personal relationships or living in lonely circumstances. Thus, in addition to having had far less psychiatric attention, patients who did not receive any drug treatment, were also less favourably placed in having been ill rather longer, in being older, deafer, and more often widowed. On the other hand, only one or two of these differences between the untreated and the treated groups approached or reached statistical significance, and the treated sample was much more heavily loaded with brain-damaged subjects. Absence of drug therapy and almost complete lack of psychiatric support were the two differences which were more likely to have caused the vastly inferior outcome of illnesses in the first sample than its slightly greater loading with potentially unfavourable prognostic factors.

Prognostic factors in patients treated with phenothiazine drugs. Patients belonging to the second and third research samples were encouraged to continue maintenance therapy as well as psychiatric support from the same doctor (the writer). It will therefore again not be possible to differentiate between the effects of medication and those of the doctor–patient relationship by a direct approach, as patients defaulting from personal supervision also tended to be poor co-operators in pill-taking. There were only a few patients who attended regularly, but were unreliable with their medications. In spite of the fact that during the second research period very strenuous efforts were made by the psychiatric social worker to bring back into treatment any defaulters, and that far less help from psychiatric social workers was available in the third period, the proportion of "unco-operative" patients remained remarkably constant, increasing only from 29·7 to 34·4 per cent, a difference fully accounted for by three patients in the last sample failing to attend the out-patient clinic after their initial appointment.

When looking for prognostic factors in patients who all had the same initial personal attention and efficient drug-therapy, we shall have to remember that long-term outcome had been very strongly related to success or failure of maintenance therapy (p. 46 and Table 15). This depended largely on co-operativeness of the patients, and each time we discover in the subsequent section a variable which appears to correlate with outcome, we shall also have to investigate whether it does so independently of the degree of co-operation maintained by the patient. Furthermore, on account of the different observation periods, we should, strictly speaking, look at our two treated samples separately. In discussing the relationship between different variables and outcome, we shall again limit ourselves to patients surviving and successfully followed up for at least one year.

Sex. Only 13 of 93 patients were men—an even lower proportion than that given by other investigators. This small number did not allow any investigation of the prognostic significance of sex.

Age. Paranoid patients (range 60–86 years) as a group were only slightly, but not significantly, older than elderly depressives admitted to the same hospital (Table 28), this difference being mainly accounted for by the greater frequency of patients over 70 in the first sample (see Table 27). "Schizophrenics" tended to be a little (insignificantly) younger than subjects diagnosed as suffering from "schizophreniform" syndromes or from paranoid hallucinosis. In addition, there was an equally insignificant tendency for younger

TABLE 28. AGE DISTRIBUTION OF ELDERLY PARANOID PATIENTS COMPARED WITH THAT OF ELDERLY DEPRESSIVES

Age	Sample		Total
	Depressives	Paranoids	
60–64	27	23	50
–69	30	28	58
–74	22	21	43
75 and over	21	21	42
	100	93	193

patients to lapse less frequently from maintenance therapy, and to progress more often along a favourable course. (Long-term outcome in this section refers only to patients who had adequate drug therapy.)

Civil status. Whereas that of elderly depressives did not differ strikingly from the marital status of the general elderly population,

TABLE 29. MARITAL STATUS OF ELDERLY PARANOID PATIENTS COMPARED WITH THAT OF DEPRESSIVES

Civil status	Sample		Total
	Depressives	Paranoids	
Married	55	25	80
Widowed	31	39	70
Separated or divorced	—	5	5
Never married	14	24	38
	100	93	193

paranoid patients, as might be expected, were more often living apart from their spouses or had never married at all (Table 29). "Schizophrenics" tended to be single, separated or divorced more frequently beyond chance expectation, whereas the widowed state was more often associated with a "schizophreniform" psychosis (Table 30, $X^2=11 \cdot 4232$; d.f.$=4$; $p< \cdot 05$). Married patients were most often successfully maintained in treatment, and single ones

TABLE 30. RELATIONSHIP BETWEEN CIVIL STATUS AND CLINICAL SYNDROME

Marital status	Clinical syndrome			Total
	Paranoid hallucinosis	Schizo-phreniform	Schizo-phrenic	
Widowed	10	22	7	39
Married	6	6	13	25
Single, separated or divorced	6	9	14	29
	22	37	34	93

least often, with widowed patients occupying an intermediate position (not significant). Married patients tended to have favourable outcomes only slightly more frequently.

Socio-occupational status. Sixty-two per cent of patients (58 of 93) belonged to the semi- and unskilled occupations, vastly more than the 12 per cent of elderly depressives in the earlier study, who showed the same predominance of skilled occupations as the younger clientele of this hospital. This finding is at first difficult to reconcile with the often attested observation that late schizophrenics tended to have had successful occupational careers (Janzarik, 1957; Klages, 1961), and had not "drifted" socially in the way of younger schizophrenics. In keeping with this, only 15 of our patients had had unstable work records, and the relatively small number of higher-class paranoid subjects in this hospital sample might have been due to their greater independence of outlook, ability to manage their entourage, and to evade treatment. In keeping with a more critical attitude towards the medical profession, members of the upper middle classes tended to lapse from maintenance more often (albeit insignificantly so) than those of the lower social groups. The comparative excess of persons of higher social status among patients with a "schizophreniform" syndrome was not significant either. The long-term outcome of higher-class patients tended to be slightly less favourable.

Intelligence was accurately assessed in only a small proportion of patients. There was an impression that below average mental endowments predominated, but this might have been due to a negative halo-effect of low social class.

Hereditary factors were as we saw earlier (pp. 31–3 and Table 5) aetiologically relatively unimportant, and also non-specific. We may now add that they did not have any prognostic implications either.

Neurotic and other deviant personality traits. Reasonably adequate information was available in 87 patients; all abnormalities were denied by their friends in 26 cases. Thirty-five persons had shown predominantly "paranoid" traits: they had been excessively sensitive, suspicious, quarrelsome, or generally hostile; a few were described as having been odd, eccentric, histrionic, or pretentious. Some of the characteristics of elderly paranoid patients described by Kay and

Roth (1961), such as failure to marry even after the birth of illegitimate children, or membership of minority cults, were not prominent in our sample, possibly because patients came from more closely-knit families. Earlier delinquency was admitted in the case of only one patient. Twenty-six had been prone to depressions and anxieties, especially concerning cleanliness and moral issues. Hypochondriacal tendencies were rare, and not a single patient had exhibited any real obsessional symptoms, such as had been clearly recognised in 18 per cent of our previous series of elderly depressives. Hysterical or phobic symptoms had not occurred during adult life in this sample of paranoid patients. No significant correlation existed between previous personality pattern and type of paranoid symptomatology, though patients with a paranoid hallucinosis were least often completely free of all personality deviations. Failure of continued co-operation was encountered a little less often in patients with only mild emotional instability (as compared with paranoid traits), who also did slightly better.

Sexual adjustment. Discussions on this subject tended to be resisted or short-circuited, as they were felt by the patients to be irrelevant to their problems. (The sexual significance of the content of their psychoses was often very obvious to the exploring psychopathologist!) Less than one-quarter of patients were still married, and reliable information on past sexual adjustment was available in only 56 per cent as against in 88 per cent of elderly depressives. A rough estimate of adjustment could be arrived at in 86 of 93 subjects; it had been satisfactory in only 28, 33 per cent as against 55 per cent of depressives, a not unexpected finding. A trend for sexually well-adjusted patients to remain in treatment more often was not significant.

Dysthymic tendencies. Information was probably reliable in 88 cases. Fifteen had histories suggestive of episodic depressions, severe enough to be remembered, but to require treatment in only three. A further 14 patients had shown milder dysthymic tendencies, frequent mood swings, outbursts of temper, or general moroseness. We are thus left with 62·5 per cent (59 of 88) without any marked previous affective abnormalities, considerably more than in elderly depressives (32 per cent). A history of definite past affective disturbance was least often (not significantly) given in patients with a paranoid hallucinosis; only 4 of the 15 patients with a background of actual affective illness failed to have depressive admixtures to their paranoid psychoses. However, depressive symptoms were very common in these illnesses (see p. 23) regardless of the absence or presence of earlier dysthymic trends.

Pattern and quality of past relationships. In keeping with the high prevalence of abnormal personality features, nearly one-third of patients had been withdrawn and suspicious in their relationships with other people; another third maintained social contacts only within the family; and less than one-third had pleasant, though largely superficial relationships with unrelated persons. An impression (Table 31) that this had been least often the case in paranoid hallucinosis cases was not confirmed by statistical tests. In spite of

TABLE 31. PERSONAL RELATIONSHIP PATTERNS RELATED TO CLINICAL SYNDROMES

Predominant relationship pattern	Clinical syndrome			Total
	Paranoid hallucinosis	"Schizo-phreniform"	"Schizo-phrenic"	
Outside family, pleasant	4	12	13	29
Family centered	8	14	10	32
Unpleasant, suspicious, withdrawn	10	8	11	29
	22	34	34	90

the restricted nature of personal contacts, these were practically non-existent or largely bad in only 39 of 93 patients, but reasonably harmonious in 54, very similar to the frequency of good interpersonal relations found in elderly depressives (61 of 96). This high proportion of paranoid old people maintaining fairly good relationships with other persons is atypical of what has been reported in the literature, and almost certainly a selection effect operating in a hospital admitting patients only informally and often after they had been persuaded by their families to come for help. We recorded earlier (Table 15) that phenothiazine therapy was successfully maintained in 39 of 65 patients, followed for at least one year. In a few, failure had been due to problems for which the patients could not be blamed (late starting of drug therapy, drug sensitisation, failure of co-operation by other doctors). Long-term co-operation had, in fact, been forthcoming in 42, and was strongly related to the presence of comparatively good

TABLE 32. RELATIONSHIP BETWEEN SUCCESS IN MAINTAINING DRUG THERAPY AND QUALITY OF PERSONAL RELATIONSHIPS

Quality of relationships	Co-operation in long-term therapy		Total
	Maintained	Not maintained	
Mainly good	32	9	41
Largely bad	10	14	24
	42	23	65

interpersonal patterns (Table 32, $X^2=7 \cdot 2451$; d.f.$=1$; $p < \cdot 01$). Patients with good relationships also tended to have a slightly better outcome with treatment.

Brain damage had not been strikingly associated with any one clinical syndrome, its greater frequency in patients with a paranoid hallucinosis being statistically insignificant (p. 23 and Table 3). Among 65 drug-treated patients surviving the first year of the follow-up, brain damage was definitely confirmed in 11; in 12 there was doubtful evidence for the occurrence of pathological cerebral changes, and in 42 no such evidence had as yet appeared. With follow-through periods varying between 12 and 41 months, statistical tests were not applied, but the figures in Table 33 suggest that really good long-term outcomes in the area of paranoid symptomatology were most frequently seen in patients remaining free of any suspicion of cerebral disorder. This poorer outcome of brain-damaged patients was not, however, associated with any special tendency on their part of lapsing from maintenance therapy.

Deafness had also been associated most frequently (but not beyond chance expectation) with paranoid hallucinosis. Only 2 among 15 drug-treated deaf patients followed for more than one year had a top outcome, as against 20 of 50 without impaired

TABLE 33. THE RELATIONSHIP BETWEEN BRAIN DAMAGE, SUCCESS IN MAINTAINING DRUG THERAPY, AND LONG-TERM OUTCOME. (PATIENTS DYING OR LOST DURING FIRST YEAR HAVE BEEN OMITTED.)

	Pathological brain changes			Total
	Confirmed	Doubtful	Absent	
Long-term outcome				
A + 1	2	2	18	22
B + 2 + 3	5	5	15	25
C + 4 + 5	4	5	9	18
	11	12	42	65
Drug-therapy co-operation				
Maintained	8	6	28	42
Not maintained	3	6	14	23
	11	12	42	65

TABLE 34. DEAFNESS, LONG-TERM OUTCOME, AND SUCCESSFUL MAINTENANCE TREATMENT

	Deafness		Total
	Present	Absent	
Long-term outcome			
A + 1	2	20	22
B + 2 + 3	7	18	25
C + 4 + 5	6	12	18
	15	50	65
Drug-therapy co-operation			
Maintained	7	35	42
Not maintained	8	15	23
	15	50	65

hearing. Deaf subjects were more frequently lost from maintenance therapy through lack of continued co-operation (Table 34).

Clinical syndrome. Long-term outcome did not relate to type of paranoid symptomatology. Patients with a "schizophreniform" syndrome, i.e. those suffering from pathological experiences more widely spread than auditory paranoid hallucinations, and yet not exhibiting Schneider's first-rank symptoms, did a little worse (Table 35). None of the differences in any combination are statistically significant. Failure in maintaining drug therapy also occurred rather more frequently in "schizophreniform" patients.

TABLE 35. TYPE OF PARANOID SYMPTOMATOLOGY RELATED TO OUTCOME AND SUCCESS OF MAINTENANCE THERAPY

	Clinical syndrome			Total
	Paranoid hallucinosis	"Schizo-phreniform"	"Schizo-phrenic"	
Long-term outcome				
A + 1	6	6	10	22
B + 2 + 3	7	9	9	25
C + 4 + 5	2	11	5	18
	15	26	24	65
Co-operation in drug therapy				
Maintained	11	13	18	42
Not maintained	4	13	6	23
	15	26	24	65

Depressive admixtures were very common, and among the 65 treated patients, who survived the first year of the follow-up, they occurred in exactly three-fifths (Table 36). The presence of depression was not, as in younger schizophrenics, associated with a better prognosis. In our sample, it was most often related to a course characterised by partial or temporary remissions, in spite of the fact that the presence of depressive admixtures appeared slightly to favour long-term co-operation in drug therapy. This tendency for depressive symptomatology to make for an indifferent outcome became even more obvious when the 17 patients with severe depression were compared with the rest. As had been hinted earlier (p. 23) a tendency for depressive features (whether slight or severe) to be present less often in "schizophrenic" as against "schizophreniform" or paranoid hallucinosis patients was slight and statistically insignificant.

TABLE 36. DEPRESSIVE FEATURES RELATED TO OUTCOME AND SUCCESS OF MAINTENANCE THERAPY

	Depressive admixtures		
	Present	Absent	Total
Long-term outcome			
A + 1	12	10	22
B + 2 + 3	18	7	25
C + 4 + 5	9	9	18
	39	26	65
Co-operation in drug therapy			
Maintained	27	15	42
Not maintained	12	11	23
	39	26	65

Duration of illness had been difficult to assess in most cases, as the condition had usually developed insiduously, and had not been related to any outstanding event in the patient's life (see p. 30).

TABLE 37. DURATION OF ILLNESS RELATED TO LONG-TERM OUTCOME AND CO-OPERATION IN TREATMENT

	Duration of illness			
	–1 year	2–3 years	4 years over	Total
Long-term outcome				
A + 1	12	4	6	22
B + 2 + 3	9	9	7	25
C + 4 + 5	8	2	8	18
	29	15	21	65
Co-operation in drug therapy				
Maintained	21	9	12	42
Not maintained	8	6	9	23
	29	15	21	65

Not too much reliance should, therefore, be placed in the figures given in Table 37, which suggest that the slight tendency for patients ill for less than one year to have good long-term outcomes more often than cases of longer duration is matched by the greater long-term co-operation shown by recently ill patients. Of greater importance is the finding that long duration of symptoms did not necessarily predict failure of drug therapy (it did not relate to clinical syndrome either).

Discussion. We saw just now that only a few variables had been to a slight extent especially associated with any one clinical syndrome (for summary of findings, see Table 38); non-paranoid personality deviations, brain damage, and deafness were a little more commonly encountered in patients with a paranoid hallucinosis as their only symptomatology; poor personal relationships and membership of

TABLE 38. RELATIONSHIP OF VARIOUS CHARACTERISTICS TO CLINICAL SYNDROME LONG-TERM OUTCOME, AND CO-OPERATION

	Paranoid hallucinosis	Schizo-phreniform syndrome	Schizo-phrenic syndrome	Better long-term co-operation	Better prog-nosis
Age below 70			+	+	+
Marital status		Widowed*	Single* Sep. Div.	Married	Married
Lower social class		−		+	+
Non-paranoid personality disorder	+			+	+
Good sex adjustment				+	+
Good relationships				+*	+
Brain damage	+			−	−
Deafness	+			−	−
Depression			−	+	−
Duration less than 1 year				+	+

Plus and minus signs indicate that the variable was particularly frequently or rarely encountered; asterisks denote that the frequency of the variable exceeded chance expectation at a significant level.

the skilled or professional classes were slightly more often associated with a "schizophreniform" psychosis; "schizophrenic" patients tended to be younger than the rest, and to exhibit depressive admixtures a little less frequently. The only statistically significant findings related to civil status; there was an "excess" of widows in "schizophreniform", and one of single, separated, or divorced persons in "schizophrenic" cases.

Patients who continued to co-operate in maintenance therapy had a strikingly better long-term outcome than those who defaulted (p. 46 and Table 15). Continued co-operation, in turn, was associated with certain variables, which thus indirectly became prognostic factors. Only one of these associations was frequent beyond chance expectation: co-operativeness was positively correlated with predominantly good relationship patterns between the patient and his entourage (Table 32). Though not to a statistically significant extent, many other characteristics of patients were associated with good long-term co-operation, and all had in common that they were likely to favour close personal relationships: relatively low age, being still married, working-class membership, only mild emotional rather than paranoid personality deviations in the past, relatively good sexual adjustment, and short duration of paranoid illness. By contrast, deafness and cerebral deterioration might be expected to impair personal relationships and they were in fact associated with poorer co-operativeness in treatment and with poorer outcome.

It is suggested that in achieving successful drug maintenance, good rapport between patient and doctor is essential, and that this was more easily achieved in patients with characteristics favouring other predominantly good relationships. The presence of mild effective and nervous complaints in the past, and of depressive feelings or thoughts obviously fostered a desire to depend on a psychiatrist. It is perhaps not too far-fetched to suggest that patients who continued to live with their spouses, those who used to have good sexual and good general personal relationships, were more likely to continue in friendly and trusting contact with their doctor. Membership of a lower social class might also favour dependence on a doctor who was willing and able to overcome class barriers. Furthermore, persons below the age of 70 were less likely to be "disengaged" (Cumming and Henry, 1961) than older ones, and patients ill for a short time presumably remained more approachable than those who had been psychotic for longer periods. Though the type of paranoid symptomatology did not possess any statistically validated prognostic significance, patients with a "schizophreniform" syndrome did somewhat less well and also defaulted from treatment more often than others (Table 35). It is noteworthy that "schizophreniform" subjects were more frequently widowed (significantly), more often on bad terms with other people and more often members of the higher social classes—features which probably interfered in this group of persons with a good patient–doctor relationship. Characteristics favouring or impeding its establishment were more evenly balanced in patients with paranoid hallucinosis or with a "schizophrenic" syndrome (Table 38).

Factors in the previous personality and clinical features apart, continued good co-operation was also significantly associated with the results achieved during the initial phase of drug therapy; it was strongly favoured by immediate and complete remission of symptoms and also by the patient achieving some degree of "insight" (p. 53; Tables 23–26).

In this analysis of results, we have so far omitted all those patients who had either been lost or who had died during the first year following reception into the study. If now we include all patients who had died, the number of those with the best long-term outcome remains unchanged at 22; mediocre results were achieved in 27 (instead of in 25), and hardly any improvement was observed in 21 (instead of 18). The chief factors associated with these results were again failure on the part of patients to co-operate (in 7 instances), mainly the fault of family doctors (in 2), severe physical illness (especially cerebral disorders), or drug idiosyncrasies (in 7). Poor results were largely unexplained by any of these factors in only 5 patients.

It is hardly necessary to point out a positive feed-back, operating in the treatment of these elderly paranoid patients. Those responding initially with a complete remission of symptoms were more likely to continue drug therapy in accordance with their psychiatrist's advice (especially when they had gained some degree of realisation concerning the abnormal nature of their past experiences and beliefs) than those who remained ill. Continued co-operation, in turn, had been found to have been the commonest factor favouring successful long-term maintenance of phenothiazines, and this again was associated with a favourable long-term outcome to a highly significant extent. Other favourable prognostic factors were all found to have acted ultimately, by promoting a good relationship with the treating psychiatrist. Completing the circle, we may add that the writer was impelled towards continuing to take a very active interest in the further management of these hitherto "hopeless cases", by the patients' good initial response to drug therapy.

The role of drug therapy might have been disentangled from the effects of supportive contact with the psychiatrist if we had replaced the drug within a double-blind design by a placebo, while keeping psychiatric contact constant. We described earlier (p. 16) why at the beginning of this investigation we had failed to carry out this design, but pointed out that in fact not a single patient starting on a placebo made a significant improvement. Substitution of the active preparation by placebo tablets at a later date, while the patient was attending the out-patient clinic, was considered but rejected. It would have entailed deceit, both of the patient and his friends, and disturbed the atmosphere of trust which had been built up. Instead, phenothiazine dosages were reduced or discontinued in patients who were doing well as often as became possible, but both the patients and their friends were told what was being done; both were positively motivated towards the experiment, as it held out the possibility of discontinuing medication, which in most instances was felt to be irksome.

Complete and apparently lasting remissions of all symptoms in the course of phenothiazine therapy were achieved in 33 patients and, at the time of writing, attempts at lowering or discontinuing maintenance dosages had been made in 29 instances. In 7 of these patients no recurrences of symptoms took place (after from 30 to 10 months; average duration of drug-free period, 20 months). These full and lasting recoveries after stopping phenothiazines were not restricted to any one subsyndrome, but 4 of 7 cases were of the "schizophrenic" type. In 15 of the remaining 22 relapsing patients, complete remission of symptoms was achieved after reinstituting drug therapy. Failure was always associated with factors interfering with resuming efficient treatment.

In concluding the clinical section of this report, it is hardly necessary to point out that we have been dealing with patients who were probably somewhat atypical of the general run of elderly people with delusional persecutory beliefs and experiences, in that they had agreed to accept psychiatric treatment. They were also less frequently and less severely isolated socially than many compulsorily admitted patients described in the reports of other investigators.

In the course of the present study, 71 patients initially received full courses of phenothiazine preparations, and these were followed by full remission of all psychiatric symptoms in 43 cases. Marked amelioration was recorded in 22, and only 6 patients remained unchanged (Table 8), though 2 did quite well later on. By contrast, only one of 22 patients not receiving adequate amounts of these drugs appeared to have experienced a good remission, with psychiatric social work, and this was maintained to the end of the observation period (in her case, 16 months). Sixty-five subjects were successfully followed-through from 12 to 41 months, most of them for 3 years. Twenty-two remained, after the initial treatment, free of all psychotic symptoms and paranoid preoccupations over the whole of the observation period; 25 exhibited symptoms for periods of varying length, and only 18 remained psychotic throughout, though in most instances less severely disordered than when first seen (Table 18).

As has been shown by other workers (e.g. most recently for chronic schizophrenics by Waters and Northover, 1965), ultimate outcome depended largely on whether or not long-term drug therapy could be maintained successfully. This, in turn, was related to factors which might have been favouring an attitude of continued co-operation with the psychiatrist on the part of the patient, especially relatively good relationships with other persons in their entourage and the gaining of some "insight" following the initial period of phenothiazine treatment. The paramount role played by these preparations in so signally improving the outlook in the paranoid illnesses of the elderly (the late schizophrenias) was further demonstrated by the finding that only 7 patients remained well up to the end of the observation period after all drugs were stopped, and that 15 patients had recurrences of symptoms, which again remitted completely after phenothiazine therapy was reinstituted.

CHAPTER 7

Theoretical Issues

It is tempting to hail the results reported in this study as an important advance in the treatment of elderly patients with psychiatric conditions of a kind hitherto regarded as virtually incurable. The way in which it had often been possible to allow symptoms of a schizophrenic type to wax and wane in response to varying the dosages of so-called psychotropic drugs was certainly impressive. On the other hand, we made the observation that many patients deteriorated socially in spite of a favourable clinical response, while others remained well integrated within their family or other social settings, even when they continued to have psychotic symptoms. We should also recall that the patients reported here were rather atypical of paranoid elderly persons, in that they at least initially co-operated in psychiatric treatment and had tolerant relations or friends who had encouraged them in this direction. The long-term success of treatment was often jeopardised when family relationships were not sufficiently close and harmonious to sustain initial interest. Emotional and social isolation, as well as hostile withdrawal, are unfortunately the leading characteristics of the general run of paranoid old people. Family doctors and community welfare workers only occasionally succeed in persuading them to commence, let alone continue treatment involving regular medication. For these reasons, adequate psychiatric supervision and maintenance treatment are at present made available to a small proportion only of elderly paranoid persons, but it is hoped that realisation of the encouraging results achieved in their treatment may stimulate doctors and welfare workers towards more sustained and successful efforts in tracing cases and persuading patients into accepting help. While acknowledging that the practical results of our investigation are likely to find only limited application for some time to come, there remains the possibility that this study of late schizophrenics and of their response to modern treatment may shed some light on the perennial problem of schizophrenia in general.

Symptomatology. Concerning the phenomenology of late schizophrenia, this investigation has done little more than to confirm that all patients with this disorder exhibited paranoid or closely related symptoms. Typical catatonic features were not encountered, but occasionally patients showed very slight mannerisms and stereotypies. Many patients were vague in their verbal communications, especially when they concerned their pathological experiences and beliefs. However, similar defects of communication can often be observed when exploring the hypochondriacal and guilt delusions of depressives, and unmistakable schizophrenic disorders of speech and of thinking were never convincingly demonstrated in the verbal productions of patients in this sample. Nearly one-third of subjects exhibited some degree of deafness and this, together with vagueness and poor enunciation due to lack of education, made mental exploration often difficult. In spite of this, it was usually possible to recognise that the patient's disorder placed him in one of three groups, characterised by symptom clusters which were graded in terms of understandability of the patient's pathological beliefs and experiences, in a manner which we shall once again place on record.

Most easily comprehended were states in which old people began to imagine that they could hear noises or even remarks, from which they concluded that they had become foci of hostile attention, and that people wanted to get rid of them. Largely auditory hallucinations and persecutory fears related to them, were the only symptoms that could be discovered in this group of patients, to whom the label of "paranoid hallucinosis" was attached. These two types of symptom were usually also present in subjects exhibiting, in addition, other kinds of abnormal experiences and preoccupations, often phantastic, but still within the range of what might have been invented by writers of mystery and horror fiction, or within culturally determined and comprehensible ideas of superstition and magic. In order to avoid the necessity of coining new terms, we provisionally labelled patients in this group as "schizophreniform". Finally, there were people we classed as "schizophrenic". As a rule, they also experienced accusatory voices and held persecutory beliefs; sometimes they suffered from more or less understandable "schizophreniform" experiences, such as unpleasant odours or lights being directed at them, or threats to safety and property. But in addition, and sometimes as the only symptomatology, these "schizophrenic" patients exhibited clinical phenomena of a less banal type and possessing the status of international currency for the diagnosis of schizophrenia: experiences of influence and passivity, of interpenetration with the environment, and of thoughts and feelings connecting them in a two-way traffic to other persons, God, or the devil; finally, there was the kind of auditory hallucinosis which alone was regarded by K. Schneider as of first-rank importance in making a diagnosis of schizophrenia—voices discussing the patient in the third person, or giving a running commentary on his thoughts and actions. Differentiation of patients with a paranoid hallucinosis alone caused little difficulty, but the borders between "schizophreniform" and "schizophrenic" were often quite difficult to draw. That there was some substance to these phenomenological subdivisions is, however, suggested by the following considerations: the way in which paranoid patients could be placed along a continuum ranging from understandable deviations to schizophrenic disintegration of many personality functions had gradually crystallised in the writer's mind in the course of his clinical observations. Also, the proportions of these three symptom clusters were very similar in all three consecutive samples of patients. Much more impressive, however, was the discovery that not a single patient with a "schizophrenic" syndrome was among that one-third of subjects who on removal from their home surroundings, lastingly ceased to have any active psychotic experiences (though not losing their false beliefs). This suggested that in the case of "schizophrenic" symptoms, one was dealing with a more deep-seated, possibly cerebrally or somatically determined disorder, much as was suggested by Astrup (1962) regarding the systematic schizophrenias of the Leonard classification. By contrast, "paranoid hallucinosis" and "schizophreniform" psychosis might be disorders which (in keeping with their symptomatology) arose perhaps from interactions between certain ageing personalities and environmental stresses, to which their later developments were especially prone to expose them. This would be in line with Haase's (1963) findings in unmarried middle-aged paranoid women.

An hypothesis of the following pattern might accordingly be advanced: "schizophrenic" psychoses could be looked upon as largely constitutionally determined late forms of schizophrenia, whereas "paranoid hallucinosis" and "schizophreniform" psychoses might be regarded as persecutory syndromes of different and differing aetiology, with important reactive or psychogenic factors. Furthermore, compared with "schizophreniform" states, paranoid hallucinosis should be regarded as a milder and more limited reaction. These hypotheses might find support if certain correlations were confirmed to exist between aetiological factors and types of symptomatology. If "schizophrenic" psychoses were more constitutionally and to a much smaller extent exogenously determined, in comparison with the other two syndromes, one might expect differences in the strength of hereditary factors. For what it is worth, we did in fact discover that 3 out of the 5 relatives with schizophrenia belonged to "schizophrenic" probands (Table 5). If, furthermore, our "schizophrenics" represented, in terms of age of onset, the tapering tail-end of a distribution curve with its maximum earlier in life, we might expect them to be on the whole younger than other elderly paranoid patients. This was in fact the case (Table 38), but not to a statistically significant extent. If "schizophrenic" pictures were predominantly constitutionally determined, one might expect them to be more typical, presenting as it were schizophrenia in pure culture and without admixtures belonging to other mental reaction types. In keeping with this suggestion, depressive symptomatology was in fact less often encountered in "schizophrenic" as compared with "schizophreniform" and "paranoid hallucinosis" patients, but only to an insignificant extent (Table 13). The only area in which "schizophrenics" stood clearly apart from the rest was that of marital status. Significantly more often than others, "schizophrenics" had never married at all or had broken marriages (Table 30), suggesting that their past sexual adjustment might have been even poorer than that of other elderly paranoid patients. This would be in line with the high celibacy rate and "chaotic sexuality" of younger schizophrenics. In keeping with our tentative hypothesis, "paranoid hallucinosis" and "schizophreniform" patients possessed, apart from their greater age, some other characteristics which might have favoured disturbances of personal relationships. Subjects with "paranoid hallucinosis" were more frequently deaf or afflicted with cerebral deteriorations (Table 38). They had been able least often to maintain harmonious social relationships outside their immediate families earlier in life, and in their case the existence of earlier personality deviations was least often denied. None of these trends was statistically significant, but "schizophreniform" symptoms occurred significantly most often in widowed persons (Table 30).

In summary, the distribution of constitutional, physical, personality, and social variables lent only very slight support to an hypothesis, according to which "schizophrenic" psychoses were largely endogenously and constitutionally determined, whereas "schizophreniform" illnesses, and to a greater extent "paranoid hallucinoses", could be more satisfactorily conceptualised as reactions of abnormal personalities to the physical and social stresses and deprivations of old age. Other findings reported earlier indicated much more impressively the special status of patients with Schneider's first-rank symptoms, classified here as "schizophrenics": the admittedly subjective impression of inadequate communication of their affective state (Table 3), and the observation that in contrast to other symptoms, those of first rank never disappeared following the patient's removal from his customary environment). In delineating our three subsyndromes, we had to admit (*pace* Schneider!) that a clear differentiation, especially between "schizophreniform" and "schizophrenic" had not always been possible. We may add now that we were unable to discover any incisive aetiological differences as between the three syndromes, leading to the opinion that they were not three disease entities, but three symptom clusters arranged along a continuum. They might be looked upon as a graduated expression of the extent to which, late in life, the schizophrenic mental reaction type had finally become clinically manifest. This suggestion that late schizophrenic illnesses should be regarded to differing degrees as partial or incomplete schizophrenias will be taken up again in the course of subsequent discussions.

Persistent Persecutory States of the Elderly

Ageing and cerebral deterioration. Until recently, views have been much in vogue according to which mental senility was not so much the result of physical cerebral deterioration, but was largely facilitated by social and personal factors. Latterly, opinions have tended to veer back in the opposite direction. Normal mental senescence on the one hand, and senile and arteriosclerotic dementia on the other, are held to be descriptively, as well as aetiologically, entirely separate and distinct conditions. Evidence favouring this view has been summarised elsewhere (Post, 1965), and the dementias of old age now tend to be regarded as definite heredo-familial diseases (Larsson, Sjoegren, and Jacobson, 1963) rather than as pathological exaggerations of normal ageing.

It is well known that transitory or persistent paranoid, schizophreniform, or schizophrenic symptoms are not infrequently seen in patients with psycho-organic syndromes, including the dementias of old age. We noted earlier that the presence of brain damage in our age group had not been especially linked with any one type of persistent paranoid symptomatology (pp. 28–9 and Table 3), and we came to the conclusion that there did not exist a specific organic or symptomatic paranoid psychosis. Like in the case of depression, the presence of both schizophrenic and psycho-organic symptoms in elderly patients was regarded as coincidental, though the possibility of precipitation was left open. It is interesting to note that Leonard and Briewig (1964) have quite independently come to the identical view in a study of elderly depressives and schizophrenics. However, occasionally, a direct causal relationship between organic process and paranoid-schizophrenic symptomatology is strongly suggested.

Mr. J. G. S., a bachelor, aged 61, lived with his brother's family. Hereditary disorders were denied, but he had always been family-centred, and after service with the Royal Corps of Signals, had found difficulty in settling down in life. For the last 20 years, however, he had held down a job as a bricklayer with the same firm. Sailing and cycling on his own were his only spare-time occupations, and he had only one woman friend, whose husband successfully cited him as co-respondent in a divorce action. He claimed innocence and denied incredibly (as we shall see presently) ever having had any sexual experience.

Nine months before admission, he began to have bouts of vomiting and malaise, and at the same time thought occasionally that television programmes were referring to him. During the days before admission he wandered away from his home and became incapable of giving any account of his movements.

On admission, he showed all the features of a subacute confusional state, which could be quantified by psychological testing, but during which he did not voice any paranoid ideas. Though physically no abnormalities were discovered in the nervous system and the EEG was normal, the patient's blood Wassermann and Kahn reactions were positive. His CSF contained 146 white blood cells mm^3, 90 per cent of which were lymphocytes; protein 60 mg per cent, globulin increased, Lange 00111000; WR positive. He accordingly received 10 million units of penicillin over 10 days, and soon after this, there was a change in his mental state; the confusion cleared (a process which was reflected in improved test performance), but at the same time he showed both elated and paranoid behaviour, initially with grandiose financial delusions, but later with a tendency to abscond from the hospital. At first, he attributed this behaviour to an irresistible impulse, but later he admitted feelings of influence, and believed that ideas were put in his head by other patients. On trifluoperazine, all psychotic symptoms disappeared and he retrospectively put them down to "imagination". At the time of discharge after a 3 months' stay, his CSF showed a negative WR; there were 16 cells mm^3, protein was still 60 mg per cent, globine slight excess, and Lange 1111000000.

The patient, who had originally shown both hypomanic and schizophrenic symptoms, became "depressed" when he tried to resume work, and imipramine was added to trifluoperazine, with presumably beneficial effect, as he was able to return to his trade (6 months after admission the CSF findings were unchanged, except that the cells had declined to 4 mm^3). Several months after all drugs were stopped and the patient had had a successful holiday abroad, he experienced strange feelings and for the first time admitted hallucinations: "men's voices telling me what to do, they would tell me to get on a bus and then say, get off now, go into King's College Hospital and have a cup of tea, don't talk, and so on". He also said he felt influenced from the outside, and that messages reached him by morse signals (see his army training!) causing flutterings of his eyelids. He lost all these symptoms with phenothiazines, but remained anergic and was readmitted. At this stage Wassermann and Kahn reactions were negative in the blood and in the CSF, which by now contained only 3 cells mm^3 normal proteins, and showed a completely flat Lange curve. Though the paranoid-schizophrenic symptoms remained controlled by phenothiazines, the patient continued to be anergic and miserable during a prolonged period of in-patient and out-patient treatment, with attempts at rehabilitation. After some months, he was referred to the care of Dr. A. J. Oldham at Cane Hill Hospital, Coulsdon, who repeated all investigations and discovered that the blood WR had again become positive (CSF findings negative in all respects). The patient had two more courses of penicillin, and when seen just over 3 years after his original admission, he was working fully and regularly as a bricklayer, and recalled with complete insight his psychotic experiences. He had not been on any medication for the preceding 14 months.

This patient's case history has been given fairly fully, because it illustrates how in the course of an organic mental illness paranoid, psycho-organic, manic, depressive, and schizophrenic reaction types successively appeared. Although this patient belonged to the geriatric age group, he suffered from a reversible organic psychosis, whose recurrence on account of insufficient treatment triggered off once again a paranoid psychosis. This responded, as far as "active" symptoms were concerned, to drug therapy, and a complete remission was achieved only after the syphilitic infection was eradicated. One is tempted to suggest that in this patient, the emergence and re-emergence of paranoid and/or schizophrenic symptoms were more sensitive indicators of persistent infection than were pathological tests!

The great majority of paranoid illnesses in late life arise in persons who appear to remain unaffected by macroscopic and microscopic cerebral changes, but who like all old people, show certain changes of personality functioning in line with increasing "disengagement" (Cumming and Henry, 1961). Ageing of personality is associated with diminution of external interests and an increasing tendency towards turning inwardly. In confirmation, scores on the Maudsley Personality Inventory indicate with rising age a decrease in "extroversion" of the general population (Shaw and Hare, 1965). Related to the reciprocal increase of "introversion" are changes with age in the pattern of minor psychiatric disorders: outwardly-directed behaviour disturbances including delinquency, conversion hysteria, and hysterical phobias are most commonly seen in the young, while hypochondriacal, ruminative, and anxious-depressive preoccupations predominate in the elderly (Post, 1965). The way in which increasing introversion, with its social repercussions, could also lead to senile character changes, and even to a paranoid psychosis, is easily envisaged.

In contrast to findings in the dementias of old age, cognitive decline in the majority of old persons is of an orderly kind (Dorken, 1958), and memory defects tend to be benign (Kral, 1962). In keeping with holistic concepts of personality, it has been possible to link cognitive with other personality changes in old age via the well-known decline in learning ability and short-term storage of information (for a detailed discussion see Welford, 1962). This decline is not necessarily associated with diminution in the number of surviving neurones but, in the absence of gross cerebral changes, might be due to defects at a molecular level. Various mechanisms have been suggested to explain defective short-term memory: premature exhaustion of circuits in brain-cell assemblies, or interference with the messenger role of ribonucleic acid molecules, in some way or other. This association of changes in molecular structures with ageing is not new (e.g. well studied in the case of connective tissue), but seems to open up new ways of looking at late schizophrenia and related disorders. So-called symptomatic schizophrenias are found in association with toxic or deficiency states which do not necessarily cause permanent cell-damage, but which affect cell functioning at the molecular level. Schizophrenic symptomatology (in a setting of unaltered awareness) associated with substances like alcohol or amphetamine is as a rule transitory. However, epilepsy is sometimes associated with persistent "symptomatic" schizophrenia, and with clinical pictures which are closely similar to those found in elderly paranoid patients. And the similarity does not stop here: the brains of elderly persons who have died in full preservation of their faculties, often contain a number of senile plaques and neurofibrillary tangles, whose significance remains unknown; similarly, the brains of epileptics may show structural changes of dubious significance, perhaps causal, but possibly secondary (anoxia) to the convulsive disorder. Fortunately, a recent study of paranoid epileptic psychoses is available for comparison with paranoid illnesses of late life.

In their publications, Slater and his fellow-workers (1963a and b) produced convincing evidence against the suggestion that epilepsy and schizophrenia might have been coincidental in their case material. They went on to show that clinically, their patients' psychiatric symptoms were often quite indistinguishable from those seen in ordinary paranoid schizophrenics, except for an unusually good preservation of affect. In contrast to our findings in elderly people, there were also some patients with a hebephrenia-like symptomatology, perhaps on account of the lower average age of onset (29·8 years) of schizophrenic symptoms in the epileptics. Though descriptively these epileptic schizophrenics were identical with "idiopathic" cases, Slater interpreted the infrequent occurrence of affective flattening or incongruity (and also his follow-up findings) to signify that these patients were not, aetiologically speaking, schizophrenics whose illness had been merely precipitated by chronic epilepsy. Other features suggesting that, on the contrary, one was dealing with schizophrenic disorders purely epileptic in origin were the high incidence (quite apart from fits) of pneumoencephalographic and of organic personality changes, the dearth of so-called schizoid traits in previous personalities, and the very small number of schizophrenic first-degree relatives (2 for 69 probands, as against an "expected" 17 among the relatives of ordinary schizophrenics—very similar to the 5 in 93 of our material). In addition, there was the discovery of an association between schizophrenic symptomatology and a special temporal lobe epilepsy of long (mean: 14 years) duration. In a discussion with Hill and Symonds (1962), Pond had drawn attention to the similarity between many subjective experiences during attacks of this type of epilepsy and some symptoms described by paranoid schizophrenics. Slater did not deny the cogency of an argument according to which abnormal experiences physically caused might become over the years integrated into, and possibly dominating, psychic life. After pursuing a succession of closely reasoned arguments, Slater and co-workers (1963b) were unable to come to a final understanding of the relationship between schizophrenic symptoms and epilepsy, but on the whole, they came to favour not a psychogenic, but a physiogenic hypothesis, according to which schizophrenic symptoms tended to occur "at a certain stage in what was in the long run a dementing process". This aetiological hypothesis could obviously be applied to schizophrenic phenomena in late life, as these also occur at a stage of a process (ageing) which might end in dementia. In effect, this development occurred only rarely in our series of late schizophrenics, but here again, there is a striking similarity with Clithero and Slater's (1963) follow-up findings in epileptic schizophrenics. Only 29 of 60 surviving epileptics (with a mean duration of schizophrenic symptoms of between 7 and 8 years) were affected by psycho-organic sequelae, and these were not strictly speaking dementias. On closer scrutiny, they consisted mainly of the kind of personality changes so often described in chronic epileptics. They had not become markedly more severe since they were first noted, and memory impairment (a defect which sooner or later becomes the most striking feature of all dementing processes) was discovered in only a few.

The following comes to mind: both in chronic temporal lobe epilepsy and during the senium, schizophrenic symptoms of a similar type (mainly paranoid with good preservation of affect) may arise, not necessarily in the setting of an obviously progressive, global dementing process associated with coarse brain changes, but within the framework of personality alterations due to far more subtle changes in cerebral function and structure. Such subtle changes may also form the physical substrate of other "symptomatic" schizophrenias, especially of amphetamine psychoses.

Drug therapy as an experimental variable. Unlike earlier studies, the present investigation was not limited to a descriptive analysis of the symptoms and course of senile schizophrenia. By introducing phenothiazine therapy, we were able to add the experimental approach. We found that adequate drug dosages almost always removed all types of paranoid symptoms occurring in the elderly, that this effect was lasting provided therapy could be effectively maintained, and that psychotic symptoms could frequently be made to wax and wane with varying intensity of drug treatment. Finally, we observed that only a few patients ultimately remained symptom-free after phenothiazines had been discontinued for good. All these findings appear at first sight to be incompatible with a physical aetiology. If progressive alterations in cerebral structure and function were the setting in which schizophrenic symptoms arose in the elderly, it would be difficult to understand how drug therapy could have a lasting effect, especially if one subscribed to the view that phenothiazine preparations merely suppressed certain kinds of schizophrenic symptoms (especially delusions and hallucinations), but that the disorder continued to erode the personality. However, recent work on acute (Kelly and Sargant, 1965) and chronic schizophrenics (Waters and Northover, 1965) followed up after phenothiazine treatment encourages a more optimistic attitude, and there have even been claims to the effect that these preparations did not just suppress psychotic symptoms, but that they interfered in their genesis in a more basic fashion. Analysing the results of a double-blind trial of several phenothiazine drugs and of a placebo on acute schizophrenics admitted to several American hospitals, Goldberg, Klerman and Cole (1965) discovered that these drugs had a more marked effect on features roughly equivalent to Bleuler's "fundamental symptoms" than on those corresponding to his "accessory symptoms", and furthermore, that "fundamental" symptoms appeared for the first time at a later stage more rarely in drug- than in placebo-treated patients. This suggested that phenothiazines not only produced a reduction of symptoms, but that they also appeared to prevent the development of "fundamental" symptoms originally not present. These authors thought that their findings were not incompatible with a hypothesis according to which one of the factors (in the presence of several others) operating to produce the clinical picture of schizophrenia was heightened physiological arousal. Its suppression by ataractic preparations might hinder the development of schizophrenic phenomena. Smythies (1963) discussed the action of phenothiazine drugs on thresholds of arousal responses more fully. Applying these considerations to our geriatric schizophrenics, one might suggest that drug-induced diminution of the state of arousal could be sufficient to abolish symptoms, even though the more basic effects of ageing on the central nervous system were still present and unaltered by the exhibition of phenothiazine preparations. In addition, affective, motivational, and volitional personality functions tended to be left relatively intact in late schizophrenia, and the removal of the largely paranoid symptoms, by whatever mechanism, should leave patients very much as they had been before they had fallen ill, that is with their long-standing personality deviations.

This expectation was confirmed by the results of the present study. Our follow-up assessment of the patients' general (social) adjustment (pp. 46–51) was particularly relevant. We recalled that in elderly depressives there had been found a highly significant correlation between clinical and social outcomes. Patients who did well clinically, almost always preserved harmonious relationships, interests and activities; deterioration in these areas was usually associated with chronicity or frequent recurrence of affective disorders. By contrast, hardly any correlation of this kind was found in elderly paraphrenics admitted to the same hospital. To a far greater extent than had been the case in elderly depressives, paranoid people had either lost family and other relationships in the course of their lives, or had preserved them in spite of their character problems, on account of other assets and/or the tolerance of their associates. The occurrence of psychotic paranoid phenomena did not appear to change relationship patterns markedly; in several instances, relatives initially embraced the patient's false beliefs and treatment was usually sought only after many months or even years, because some crisis had occurred. At a later stage, success or failure of treatment quite often related to social progress in a paradoxical fashion, in that social decline might occur in spite of removal of symptoms, and vice versa. Furthermore, relatives frequently failed to bring back relapsing patients, but would rather tolerate once again their complaints and allegations. Admittedly, a follow-up more extended than had been possible in the present investigation might have revealed that persistent paranoid symptomatology would ultimately result in severe social deterioration, either on account of psycho-organic, dementing developments, or related to schizophrenic, affective and volitional personality involvement. A complete follow-up to death was achieved in a proportion of Kay and Roth's (1961; Kay, 1963) untreated and mostly institutionalised cases. Many were reported as having deteriorated in a schizophrenic fashion, but the authors themselves pointed out how difficult it had been, especially on the basis of other peoples' case notes, to differentiate between the various types of deterioration in deaf, physically declining, and otherwise handicapped mental hospital inmates. On the whole, there is a strong impression that psycho-organic or schizophrenic deteriorations are long delayed or absent in the case of most elderly paraphrenics, and that they stand out from members of other geriatric categories by virtue of their robust physical health, long survival, and persistent mental alertness.

At present, most evidence tends to favour the view that paranoid-schizophrenic symptoms, arising for the first time late in life, are relatively isolated phenomena, which affect only limited aspects of the personality. They may arise in association with gross brain changes, but also in the course of apparently healthy ageing. Removal of mental symptoms, in the course of successful treatment with psychotropic drugs, returns patients to their previous level of functioning, and there is no clear evidence that schizophrenic deterioration will occur at a later stage.

CHAPTER 8

Some Contributions to the Study of Schizophrenia

The origins of most schizophrenic illnesses are lost in the mists of childhood or the squalls of adolescence. The late variety arises, so to speak, in the clear afternoon light of maturity and for this reason alone could be expected to yield findings which might illuminate at least some aspects of the perennial problem of schizophrenia. Pooling our observations with those of other workers, the following are the main established features of the schizophrenic reaction type, as seen during the second half of life.

Late, as contrasted with early, schizophrenics did not show any measurable characteristics of body-build which set them apart from affective psychotics. Some workers (Hirschmann and Klages, 1957) reported in a proportion of elderly schizophrenics physical stigmata of an "inter-sex type", as well as other features resembling the "dysplastic" characteristics of younger patients; but these views were only of an impressionistic kind, and were not confirmed by more precise anthropometric studies (Lodge-Patch, Post and Slater, 1965). There is general agreement concerning hereditary factors: late onset schizophrenics have slightly more schizophrenic first-degree relatives than healthy subjects, but far fewer than probands with early onsets of the illness. In the present study, there were at least three times as many first-degree relatives with affective as against schizophrenic disorders, and depressive admixtures were frequently (in 53 of 93 patients) seen in what were regarded as essentially non-affective paranoid illnesses. Assessments of previous personality features are always suspect in these patients, often without or with unduly tolerant informants. All investigators agree, however, that most patients had been in one way or other deviant. While often quite successful within their working careers, patients tended to fail in their more intimate relationships, especially psychosexually. A sizable proportion had for many years exhibited traits which could be classed as "schizoid" or "paranoid", but in contrast to what was found in elderly depressives, well-developed psychoneurotic disorders had hardly ever been prominent during the lives of the present sample of elderly paranoid persons. Illnesses diagnosed as schizophrenic and first arising between the ages of 40 and 60 appeared to follow quite frequently, hard upon emotional disturbances (Klages, 1961—many of his patients were admitted after suicidal attempts). But, in our cases of later onset, it had been much more difficult than in elderly depressives to pin-point the beginning of the illness, and to differentiate emotional causes from the effects produced by long-standing personality deviations on the patient's life situation, or from the early signs of his psychosis. Deafness was a defect which was definitely present in elderly paranoid persons much more frequently than "expected". Cerebral disease and deterioration, whether of the acute and largely reversible or of the slowly progressive and irreversible kind, were not infrequently associated at some stage with symptoms belonging to the schizophrenic type of reaction, and just as in the case of amphetamine intoxication or of temporal lobe epilepsy, they might be indistinguishable from those seen in "idiopathic", "process" or "nuclear" schizophrenia. The pathoplastic role of age, to which has been attributed the fact that hebephrenic and catatonic symptoms were more and more replaced by paranoid ones during the third and fourth decades, could be seen to continue into the period of life under investigation, when affective, volitional, and psychomotor symptoms of schizophrenia tended to be vestigial, and the clinical picture became dominated by persecutory phenomena. In the present study, it was thought possible to distribute individual patients in accordance with their symptomatology along a continuum. At one end, there were those patients with paranoid beliefs and, usually auditory, hallucinations which were understandable in terms of deafness, loneliness, and infirmity, and the contents of which were banal and very much anchored in reality. At the other extreme, experiences and beliefs were of a kind which suggested deep-going disintegration of personality functions, resulting also in the emergence of archaic mental contents and in dissolution of ego boundaries. These were the type of phenomena which would lead to a diagnosis of paranoid schizophrenia by psychiatrists of all schools and all over the world. In between those two extremes, were patients whose pathological experiences and preoccupations exceeded the limits and related contents of an hallucinosis, and yet remained understandable in terms of culturally current fantasies. Though clinical features, on the present investigator's assessment, tended to cluster either at the extremes or near the centre of a continuum, there was only slight evidence to suggest that they might represent discrete disease entities, with invariably, sharply differentiated symptomatology, and with clear-cut differences of causation and outcome.

These observations in late schizophrenics appear to fit the kind of aetiological framework recently outlined by Manfred Bleuler (1963). After looking back on 50 years of research, he wound up as follows:

> For half a century the principal aim of students of schizophrenia was assured: they sought to discover the single cause of a disease whose symptomatology and course seemed to suggest one single entity. These studies, however, were not successful. They did not lead one step nearer to the discovery of a specific cause of the hypothetical disease entity, schizophrenia. To-day we have to ask ourselves why a specific cause of schizophrenia has not been found. The reason may be simple: perhaps none exists! There may be many different pathogenic factors, together responsible for the outbreak of the disease. Just as we cannot explain the development of the healthy personality by considering a single normal influence, we cannot understand the development of schizophrenia by considering a single damaging influence. In either case, we have to deal with an integration of many dispositions and many influences.

Bleuler suggested that even in healthy people, there was

> some disposition in the direction of schizophrenic psychic life and that such disposition [might] perhaps be a normal part of human nature. This, indeed, has been proved by research into the psychology of the healthy: beneath the surface of healthy psychic life, enabling us to adapt to others and to the real world, there is hidden in every man a chaotic inner life which goes on without consideration of reality. This chaotic and illogical inner life cannot be distinguished from the schizophrenic way of thinking, imagining and living. Perhaps we may conclude: the symptomatology of schizophrenic psychoses is not always the same resulting from a common cause, but is always of the same type, because schizophrenic disease reveals the same human tendencies.

Bleuler's suggestion that schizophrenic-like forms of life exist in a hidden form in the healthy and that very different forces may destroy the dams protecting the healthy from being overwhelmed by this chaotic schizophrenic life, is paralleled by some of the suggestions made by Smythies (1963) in the course of his review of the chemistry, metabolism, and treatment of schizophrenia. He thought that there might be several types of biochemical factors in the causation of the schizophrenias. After discussing several of them, he goes on:

> Then, again, a possibility arises from this discussion that the metabolic disorders associated with schizophrenia, or at any rate some of them, may not be uniquely associated with clinical schizophrenia in any qualitative sense. They may occur in a lesser form in the metabolism of schizoid people, or in the metabolism of normal people undergoing complex and painful ego-damaging emotions, or even in the symptom-free relatives of schizophrenics. The chemical distinction between these groups may only be qualitative or regional. In the non-schizophrenics, the aberrant metabolic processes may never reach the pitch required to "break bounds" and invade the whole cerebral mechanism of perception, thinking, emotional and motor control as they seem to do in schizophrenia.

This suggestion made both from psychological and physiological points of departure, that schizophrenia may be dormant in many persons, but may become manifest in certain circumstances, tempts one to theorise on matters such as the causation, symptomatology, and response to treatment of genuine, idiopathic, pseudoneurotic, symptomatic, late, senile, and many other schizophrenias.

In pursuing this line, it is helpful to envisage some gradations of the way in which personality may be overwhelmed by schizophrenic ways of experiencing, thinking, imagining, feeling, and communicating. Young patients tend to suffer from the more complete forms of the disorder. Disintegrations of affect, thinking processes, and ego-boundaries are strongly in evidence, and perhaps prevent the further development of normal personality functions. In view of the totally disordered behaviour, abnormal appearance, and psychomotor functioning of these patients, the frequency with which biochemical pathological findings have been reported (especially in this group) is hardly surprising. Hereditary factors of schizophrenia are clearly in evidence (even though not all identical twins are concordant for the disease) but, in addition, the patients tend to have been surrounded since early childhood by other persons, mainly parents and siblings, who were themselves schizophrenics, or more often "schizoid", "paranoid" or otherwise psychologically deviant. To give but one example, Alanen (1958) discovered that 12 per cent of mothers of young male schizophrenics had been or still were psychotic, mainly schizophrenic, that 11 per cent exhibited anxiety, behaviour patterns, or unrealistic ways of thinking which bordered on the psychotic, that 40 per cent were severely and 21 per cent were moderately severely neurotic. Only 16 per cent of the mothers of these schizophrenics were more or less normal. Mothers of control neurotics and of normals were far more rarely and far less severely disturbed. Fathers were less intensively studied, but 25 per cent were alcoholics and 12 per cent exhibited morbid jealousy. In the sample studied by Lidz and his group (1958), many fathers were paranoid or given to paralogical and irrational behaviour, which dominated or seriously affected the family. These and other workers commented on the frequency with which the marriages of the parents of young schizophrenics were disturbed, but held together all the same. It has been suggested that many central symptoms of schizophrenia can be derived from a failure to learn in this kind of family setting normal relatedness to other people, as well as the achievement of personal identity (Lidz *et al.*, 1958; Wynne *et al.*, 1958; Wynne and Thaler Singer, 1963—to mention only some key references). This is not the place to try and disentangle the role of heredity from that of early environmental influences or to evaluate the claim that, among sibships, those tended to become schizophrenics who had been especially exposed to disturbing parental behaviour or interactions (Gerard and Siegel, 1950; Alanen, 1958). However, we may soon come to realise that there are no really fundamental differences between "nature" and "nurture", in that biological memory, as laid down in the chromosomal genetic code, and personal memory, the result of post-natal learning (including the shaping of personality through childhood experiences) may both be the results of similar and related intracellular mechanisms. The main point to note is that in young schizophrenics with well-established illnesses, many workers have demonstrated the presence of highly unfavourable factors acting early in life. Following Bleuler's lead, we might suggest that in their case there had been an especially strong endowment with "schizophrenic-like forms of life", and that the development of overt early schizophrenia on impact with the outside world had been prepared by harmful and potentiating family interactions. The suggestion made by Bleuler, that schizophrenic mechanisms lay ready-made in many people, even those who would not develop schizophrenia, has found support through a recent observation by Connell (1965). He studied intensively a small group of adolescents who had been referred for the treatment of amphetamine dependence. They were not psychotic, but they and their informants described in every case the occurrence of short-lasting episodes ("the horrors") during which they had delusional and hallucinatory experiences of a paranoid-schizophrenic type.

Persistent schizophrenic illnesses first manifesting themselves later on in life tend to be more often than at earlier ages episodic, recoverable, and limited to certain symptom complexes (mainly the paranoid one), with much less disturbance in the psychomotor and affective spheres, as well as in formal thinking. A full discussion of this matter would entail a complete review of subjects like "pseudoneurotic schizophrenia", which is often relatively mild and limited in the degree of personality involvement, of "puerperal schizophrenia", which is frequently recoverable, of the relationships between and ultimate outcomes of "paranoia", "paranoid schizophrenia", and "paraphrenia". These disorders all have in common past histories of personality functioning which had not been grossly deviant or disordered, perhaps exhibiting only some psychoneurotic propensities or psychosexual defects. Schizophrenic ways of life appear to be mobilised following on acute emotional events (e.g. childbirth) or emerge gradually as a result of mutually reinforcing interactions between changing personalities and increasingly rejecting social environments. Another set of causal factors is related to brain changes, ranging from gross cerebral trauma or destruction by inflammatory processes (e.g. GPI) to more localised or subtle alterations associated with epilepsy (especially the temporal lobe variety), and to intoxications (alcohol, amphetamine). Psychotic pictures associated with any of these processes are usually called "symptomatic schizophrenia" and are characterised by a paranoid symptomatology, rather than by catatonic features or disruptions of formal thinking. The schizophrenias of old age exhibit a similar symptomatology and may be equally understood as incomplete forms of the disorder. They can occur in the wake of presenile, senile or arteriosclerotic dementia; they may be triggered off by more subtle processes of cerebral ageing, and an additional factor may be an increasingly alienating interplay between the patient's introverting personality and his entourage.

The suggestion that late paraphrenia should be looked upon as a partial or incomplete form of schizophrenia is strengthened by hereditary-genetic considerations. We saw that in the schizophrenias with late onset hereditary factors were present, but very much weaker than in patients where "schizophrenic ways of life" had broken surface at an earlier age. Many late paraphrenics were shown to have exhibited deviant personality traits earlier in life, especially failure to form satisfactory close relationships. Kay and Roth (1961) suggested that these personality defects might have been caused by genetic schizophrenic features, which had not been sufficiently strong to cause an overt psychosis at an earlier age. Kay (1963) has pursued this idea further, by adducing from the literature evidence in favour of a polygenic rather than a monogenic hypothesis for the aetiology of schizophrenia. Polygenic mechanisms in the transmission of a trait (in the present context, of predisposition to schizophrenia) are associated with a continuous variation of its strength. Accordingly, one can conceive of a threshold in the strength of the predisposition, below which overt schizophrenia will not manifest itself. Kay goes on to suggest that cases of late paraphrenia occur because the threshold of illness has been lowered by "poor social and sexual adjustment". However, these may themselves have been the result of a pre-schizophrenic disposition, and it would appear to us that some additional factors would have to be looked for to avoid circular reasoning. The following might be thought of as lowering the illness threshold, and thus allowing for the first time late in life the break-through of schizophrenic ways of psychological functioning: gross cerebral disease and deterioration (causing "symptomatic" schizophrenia); the more subtle (? molecular) effects of cerebral ageing; ageing in general; potentiation of psycho-social isolation by increasing deafness, or through increasing alienation from the human environment in the wake of senile character changes of a previously deviant personality, to mention only a few possibilities.

The conception of senile schizophrenia as a partial or incomplete variety of the disorder is particularly apposite on account of its limited, "paraphrenic" type, and is also in keeping with the way in which the symptoms distribute themselves along a continuum: many patients exhibit a very imperfect schizophrenic disorder consisting of an auditory hallucinosis alone, and often limited to certain situations; others have more fantastic experiences which remain, however, understandable within the patient's cultural and educational setting. We found in only about a third of patients that the phenomena which they exhibited shaded over into those encountered in classical paranoid schizophrenia. Even they did not exhibit marked affective and personality change of a schizophrenic kind. Another finding confirming the partial nature of schizophrenic disorders in late life was the very frequent presence of important depressive admixtures. Finally, there exists the impression that older patients appear to respond much better to modern drug therapy than younger ones, and this again is in keeping with the concept of partial schizophrenia as characterising the late onset variety. Symptoms in the elderly thus tend to be localised and to affect only limited areas of personality functioning. Their suppression or extinction amounts to a cure. Sometimes, symptoms can be made to disappear by removing factors apparently responsible for their actual precipitation; e.g. by bringing old people from lonely home surroundings into conditions of communal living. Occasionally, the disease appears to be abolished by judicious manipulation of relationships. In the present series, this appears to have succeeded in only one instance (see p. 39), but other workers (e.g. Sheps, 1958) stake bigger claims. Regardless of type of schizophrenic symptomatology, phenothiazine therapy presents a highly effective procedure, which results practically always in a return to previous levels of mental health, provided it is successfully maintained over many months, possibly years.

In the closing paragraph of our review of previous work (p. 11) we quoted Kay and Roth (1961) to the effect that late paraphrenia should be regarded as the mode of manifestation of schizophrenia in old age. We may wind up our discussion by suggesting that this mode of manifestation may now be specified by the terms "partial" or "incomplete". In the past, it had been customary to regard paranoia and paraphrenia as forms of schizophrenia, which were diffusely attenuated by constitutional factors such as pyknic body-build, cyclothymic or syntonic temperament, and diminished or delayed penetrance of the abnormal gene. As has been pointed out in the preceding pages, the present study has shown that in the elderly, the removal of clearly circumscribed symptom complexes by pharmacological action on the brain resulted in a full return to previous levels of personality functioning and adjustment. This would seem to strengthen an hypothesis according to which in late schizophrenia the attenuation of pathogenes was not a general one, but that various combinations of polygenetic and exogenous factors produced specific and isolated psychological symptoms. To look upon schizophrenia of old age as a partial and discretely, rather than a generally, attenuated form of the disorder lends support to a view which regards schizophrenic ways of experiencing, feeling and thinking as maladaptive types of mental life, which to a differing and probably genetically determined extent, are present in many, perhaps in all, human beings. According to this theory, the actual manifestation of these trends as a psychosis would depend for its timing and degree of completeness on many factors, such as amount of heredity, deleterious influences in childhood (especially those emanating from deviant parents), emotional stresses of adult life, social isolation, sensory defects, "normal" ageing, and finally, different kinds of cerebral dysfunctioning, disease, or deterioration.

References

ALANEN, Y. O. (1958), The mothers of schizophrenic patients, *Act. Psychiat. Scand.* Suppl. 124.

ASTRUP, C. (1962), *Schizophrenia: Conditional Reflex Studies.* Thomas, Springfield.

ASTRUP, C., FOSSUM, A. and HOLMBOE, R. (1962), *Prognosis in the Functional Psychoses*, Thomas, Springfield.

BLEULER, M. (1943), Die spaetschizophrenen Krankheitsbilder, *Fortschr. Neurol. Psychiat.*, **15,** 259.

BLEULER, M. (1963), Conception of schizophrenia within the last fifty years and today, *Proc. Roy. Soc. Med.*, **56,** 945–52.

CLITHERO, E. and SLATER, E. (1963), The schizophrenia-like psychoses of epilepsy: IV. Follow-up record and outcome, *Brit. J. Psychiat.*, **109,** 134–42.

CONNELL, P. H. (1965), The assessment and treatment of adolescent drug takers with special reference to the amphetamines, *Proc. Leeds Sympos. Behav. Disord.* May & Baker.

CUMMING, ELAINE and HENRY, W. E. (1961), *Growing Old*, Basic Books, New York.

DAVIDSON, R. (1964), Paranoid symptoms in organic disease, *Geront. clin.*, **6,** 93–100.

DORKEN, H. (1958), Normal senescent decline and senile dementia: Their differentiation by psychological tests, *Med. Serv. J. Canada*, **14,** 18.

FAERGEMAN, P. M. (1963). *Psychogenic Psychoses*, London.

FISH, F. (1958), Leonhard's classification of schizophrenia, *J. Ment. Sci.*, **104,** 943–71.

FISH, F. (1960), Senile schizophrenia, *J. Ment. Sci.*, **106,** 938–46.

FUNDING, T. (1961), Genetics and paranoid psychoses in late life, *Act. Psychiat. Scand.* **37,** 267–82.

GERARD, D. L. and SIEGEL, J. (1950), The family background of schizophrenics, *Psychiat. Quart.*, **24,** 45–73.

GOLDBERG, S. C., KLERMAN, G. L. and COLE, J. O. (1965) Changes in schizophrenic psychopathology and ward behaviour as a function of phenothiazine treatment, *Brit. J. Psychiat.*, **111,** 120–33.

HAASE, H. J. (1963), Zur Psychodynamik und Pathoplastik paranoider und paranoid-halluzinatorischer Psychosen bei alleinstehenden Frauen, *Fortschr. Neurol. Psychiat.*, **31,** 308–22.

HILL, D., POND, D. and SYMONDS, C. (1962), The schizophrenic-like psychoses of epilepsy, *Proc. Roy. Soc. Med.*, **55,** 311.

HIRSCHMANN, J. and KLAGES, W. (1957), Konstitutionsspezifische Leitlinien bei den Psychosen des hoeheren Lebensalters, *Arch. Psychiat. Zschr. ges. Neurol.*, **196,** 254.

HOUSTON, F. and ROYSE, A. B. (1954), Relationship between deafness and psychotic illness, *J. Ment. Sci.*, **100,** 990–3.

HUNTER, R., EARL, C. J. and THORNICROFT, SYLVIA (1964), An apparently irreversible syndrome of abnormal movements following phenothiazine medication, *Proc. Roy. Soc. Med.*, **57,** 758–62.

JANZARIK, W. (1957), Zur Problematik schizophrener Psychosen im höheren Lebensalter, *Nervenarzt*, **28,** 535.

References

KAY, D. W. K. (1963), Late paraphrenia and its bearing on the aetiology of schizophrenia, *Act. Psychiat. Scand.*, **39,** 159–69.

KAY, D. W. K., BEAMISH, P. and ROTH, M. (1964), Old age mental disorders in Newcastle upon Tyne: Part II: A study of possible social and medical causes, *J. Ment. Sci.*, **110,** 668–82.

KAY, D. W. K. and ROTH, M. (1961), Environmental and hereditary factors in the schizophrenias of old age ("Late Paraphrenia") and their bearing on the general problem of causation in schizophrenia, *J. Ment. Sci.*, **107,** 649–86.

KELLY, D. H. W. and SARGANT, W. (1965), Present treatment of schizophrenia—A controlled study, *Brit. Med. J.*, **1,** 147–50.

KILPATRICK, R. and WHYTE, J. H. S. (1965), Side-effects of phenothiazine drugs, *Brit. Med. J.*, **1,** 316.

KLAGES, W. (1961), *Die Spaetschizophrenie*, Enke, Stuttgart.

KLEIST, K. (1913), Die Involutionsparanoia, *Allg. Z. Psychiat.*, **70,** 1–134.

KOLLE, K. (1931), *Die primaere Verruecktheit*, Thieme, Leipzig.

KRAL, V. A. (1962), Senescent forgetfulness: Benign and malignant, *Canad. Med. Ass. J.*, **86,** 257.

LARSSON, T., SJOEGREN, T. and JACOBSON, G. (1963), Senile dementia, *Act. Psychiat. Scand.*, Suppl. 167.

LECHLER, H. (1950), Die Psychosen der Alten, *Arch. Psychiat. Nervenkr.*, **185,** 465.

LEONARD, K. and BRIEWIG, EVA-MARIA (1964), Aetiologische Differenzierung von Depressionen jenseits des 60. Lebensjahres, *Arch. Psychiat. Zschr. d. ges. Neurol.* **205,** 358–74.

LIDZ, T., CORNELISON, ALICE R., TERRY, DOROTHY and FLECK, S. (1958), The intra-familiar environment of the schizophrenic patient: The transmission of irrationality, *A.M.A. Arch. Neurol. Psychiat.*, **79,** 309–16.

LODGE-PATCH, I. C., POST, F. and SLATER, P. (1965), Constitution and the psychiatry of old age, *Brit. J. Psychiat.*, **111,** 405–13.

MAYER-GROSS, W. (1932), *Die Schizophrenie* (IV. Die Klinik; V. Erkennung und Differentialdiagnose), in Bumkes *Handbuch der Geisteskrankheiten*, Spez. 5, Springer, Berlin.

MILLER, H. C. (1963), *The Ageing Countryman*, National Corporation for the Care of Old People, London.

MUELLER, C. (1959), *Ueber das Senium der Schizophrenen*, Karger, Basel.

PARSONS, P. L. (1964), Mental health of Swansea's old folk, *Brit. J. Prevent. Soc. Med.*, **19,** 43–7.

POST, F. (1944), Some problems arising from a study of mental patients over the age of sixty, *J. Ment. Sci.*, **90,** 554–65.

POST, F. (1962), *The Significance of Affective Symptoms in Old Age*, Maudsley Monograph **10,** Oxford University Press, London.

POST, F. (1962a), The impact of modern drug treatment on old age schizophrenia, *Geront. Clin.*, **4,** 137–46.

POST, F. (1965), *The Clinical Psychiatry of Late Life*, Pergamon Press, Oxford.

REMY, M. (1962), Emploi prolongé des neuroleptiques en psychiatrie, *Praxis* (*Rev. Suisse Med.*), **11,** 288.

ROTH, M. (1955), The natural history of mental disorders in old age, *J. Ment. Sci.*, **101,** 281–301.

ROTH, M. and MORRISSEY, J. D. (1952), Problems in the diagnosis and classification of mental disorders in old age, *J. Ment. Sci.*, **98,** 66–80.

RUEMKE, H. C. (1963), Ueber alte Schizophrene, *Schweiz. Arch. Neurol. Neurochirurg. Psychiat.*, **91,** 201–10.

References

SCHNEIDER, K. (1959), *Clinical Psychopathology* (Transl. 1953 Edn.), Grune & Stratton, New York.

SCHIMMELPENNING, G. W. (1965), Die paranoiden Psychosen der zweiten Lebenshaelfte, *Biblotheca Psychiat. Neurol.*, Fasc. 128, Karger, Basel, New York.

SHAW, G. K. and HARE, E. H. (1965), The Maudsley Personality Inventory (short form): Distribution of scores and test-retest reliability in an urban population, *J. Ment. Sci.*, **111,** 226–35.

SHELDON, J. H. (1948), *The Social Medicine of Old Age*, Oxford University Press, London.

SHEPS, J. (1958), Paranoid mechanisms in the aged, *Psychiatry*, **21,** 399.

SJOEGREN, H. (1964), Paraphrenic, melancholic and psychoneurotic states in the presenile–senile period of life, *Act. Psychiat. Scand.*, Suppl. 176.

SLATER, E., BEARD, A. W. and CLITHERO, E. (1963a), The schizophrenia-like psychoses of epilepsy: I. Psychiatric aspects, *Brit. J. Psychiat.*, **109,** 95–112.

SLATER, E., BEARD, A. W. and CLITHERO, E. (1963b), The schizophrenia-like psychoses of epilepsy: V. Discussion and conclusions, *Brit. J. Psychiat.*, **109,** 143–50.

SMYTHIES, J. R. (1963), *Schizophrenia: Chemistry, Metabolism and Treatment*, Thomas, Springfield.

WATERS, M. A. and NORTHOVER, J. (1965), Rehabilitated long-stay schizophrenics in the community, *Brit .J. Psychiat.*, **111,** 258–67.

WELFORD, A. T. (1962), On changes of performance with age, *Lancet*, **1,** 335.

WILLIAMSON, J., STOKOE, I. H., GRAY, SALLIE, FISHER, MARY and SMITH A. (1964), Old people at home: Their unreported needs, *Lancet*, **1,** 1117–20.

WYNNE, L. C., RYCKOFF, I. M., DAY, JULIANA and HIRSCH, S. I. (1958), Pseudomutuality in the family relations of schizophrenics, *Psychiatry*, **21,** 205–20.

WYNNE, L. C. and THALER SINGER, MARGARET (1963), Thought disorder and the family relations of schizophrenics: I. A research strategy, *Arch. Gen. Psychiat.*, **9,** 191–8.

Index

Index